the mothe

THE
EXPECTANT
FATHER

Dr David Haslam

SUMMER LEAVE '93!!
Darling Tim,
The excitment of 'ALL
THIS', the nervousness & fears,
joys & pleasures to come.
It makes me realise that
there is noone else in the
world, I would want to
share this with.
To the 'BEST' man I know &
love.

Conran Octopus

Project editor	Jane O'Shea
Editor	Carole McGlynn
Art editor	Peter Cross
Project assistant	Dawn Sirett
Production	Sonya Sibbons
Illustrators	Terry Mckenna
	Lucy Su
	Will Giles and Sandra Pond
Jacket photograph	Julie Fisher

First published in 1990 by
Conran Octopus Limited
37 Shelton Street,
London WC2H 9HN

Reprinted 1991, 1992 (twice), 1993

ISBN 1 85029 260 4

Typeset by Litho Link Ltd, Powys, Wales
Printed in Hong Kong

Contents

Introduction

So you are going to be a father! It is a wonderful feeling – a mixture of pride, elation and happiness, not to mention a fair sprinkling of anxiety, confusion and sheer blind panic. I know just how you feel.

You will certainly be in for some changes. Whether this is your first pregnancy or your fourth, nothing will be quite the same again. Times like this can be a source of great strength for a relationship, and the more you understand about your partner's pregnancy the better. After all, attitudes to the father's role are changing all the time. Your part in the proceedings did not finish with the fun of conception. You have a great deal more to offer than that.

If fathers don't make an effort to understand pregnancy and childbirth, then they will inevitably miss out on many of the joys and pleasures that are in store. You will feel an outside spectator, not an essential part of the proceedings. Your partner needs your help and support, and you will enjoy the next few months far more if you take an active interest. Reading this book is an excellent first step.

You are bound to have plenty of questions. How will our lives change? What actually happens in labour? Where should the baby be born? How will it affect us financially? Is it goodbye to sex for the next few months? This book will look at all these questions, particularly from the father's point of view. Sadly, many books on pregnancy do not even mention the word 'father' in the index, but today many fathers take a very active part in all aspects of childcare. It may have been true in the past that men took a very peripheral role in the whole business of child rearing, but everyone is now well aware of the great advantages for the whole family when fathers become more involved.

You are bound to feel confused and uncertain about what is in store during the next few months – and you are not the only one to feel this way. Even though I had already qualified as a doctor when my wife first became pregnant, I well remember the confusion and doubts that I felt at that time. Every father worries that he will be the one who will embarrass everyone by fainting during the delivery and there cannot be a father who was not terrified that he would drop his baby the first time he took it in his arms. Every father worries, and you will be the same.

But this book will help you to worry less. If you dress in lightweight clothes for the delivery room, for example, the chances of your feeling faint will be greatly reduced. And how often have you actually heard of a baby being dropped by its parents? I can't think of a single occasion, but it didn't stop me holding my newborn daughter as gently and nervously as if she were a piece of crumbly fruit cake. Most of your worries and fears will turn out to be unnecessary, and fatherhood will become a source of genuine joy.

USING THIS BOOK

This book will not attempt to give a detailed account of the day by day development of the baby, nor a scientific description of modern obstetric care. Your partner is bound to have books on pregnancy, and that is where you will find this type of information. Do read as much as you can about the subject. This is one aspect of life where a little knowledge is certainly not a dangerous thing. The more you know about the developing baby the better. In addition, it obviously helps you both tremendously if you also understand and appreciate the changes your partner is experiencing. However, while obviously touching on all these important topics, the aim of *The Expectant Father* is to concentrate on *your* part in the next few months – what you have to offer, and how you can help, as well as answering the questions and worries that fathers have.

Throughout this book I shall refer to the mother-to-be as your 'partner' since many parents today are not married, and this term covers girlfriends as well as wives. This choice of word seemed simpler than any other, but I apologize if any married readers feel offended by it. Similarly, 'he' and 'she' are used in alternate chapters when writing about the baby. I know many expectant couples refer to their unborn child as 'it', but in print this seems more than a little impersonal.

Finally, congratulations! Enjoy your pregnancy, and use this book to make the whole mysterious process just a little less confusing. By the end of it you will be changing nappies like an expert – something you would once never have believed.

What's going on?

Pride and panic. It's quite a combination, and one known to every new father. Becoming a parent is inevitably one of the high spots of anyone's life: family and friends offer their congratulations, and your life changes for ever.

A common cliché in films and novels is that moment when the irresponsible young man discovers that his wife is pregnant, promptly abandons his worldly ways, and settles down to decorating the nursery and helping his partner choose the layette. The image is a powerful one – though often short-lived. Parenthood brings responsibilities and worries, as well as joy and happiness. The more you understand about what your partner is going through, and why, the easier it will be for you both to cope with all the changes.

At the beginning of any pregnancy, while you will be feeling pride or panic, or a mixture of both, your partner will be more deeply affected by the changes in her body. From the moment of conception, hormonal changes may affect her mood and her physical well-being in various ways. It is vitally important to realize that these changes are beyond her control. If your partner has suffered from the pre-menstrual tension syndrome in the past, you will already be well aware of the effects that hormones can have on both your lives. Some women describe this as being like Jekyll and Hyde, and many men know just what they mean.

Early on in a pregnancy, wild fluctuations of mood are very common. These range from elation and happiness to the depths of despair and depression, irritability and anger. Your partner cannot help the way she feels, and will probably feel guilty if she is snappy and tense with you. Indeed, she may say things that she later regrets and never meant in the first place. Simply understanding and accepting why she feels the way she does can help enormously.

Physical symptoms

Apart from being emotionally fragile, certain physical symptoms are very common in these early weeks:

▶ Tender, sore, and probably swollen breasts
▶ Nausea – not just in the mornings, but at any time of day
▶ Tiredness, especially in the evenings
▶ Difficulty in concentrating
▶ Being unable to tolerate the taste of tea or coffee
▶ Other physical symptoms can include backache, bleeding gums, constipation, heartburn, piles, varicose veins and stretch marks.

These various symptoms frequently have another effect. It is difficult to enthuse about the forthcoming baby if you are feeling literally sick and tired, and many women then worry that their lack of enthusiasm may be somehow abnormal. Talk to your partner, listen to her worries, and reassure her that such feelings are very common.

Some expectant fathers can also feel emotionally flat. At the start of pregnancy everything can seem unreal, and it may take a while to appreciate what is going on in both your lives. If you feel numb rather than excited at the moment, don't worry. There's plenty of time to come to terms with the idea of parenthood and indeed to become enthusiastic about it.

COPING WITH NAUSEA

Nausea, the traditional morning sickness, can be very distressing during the first two or three months when it affects half of all pregnant women. If it is severe, your partner should see her doctor, but there is plenty that you can do to help. Many women find that eating a dry biscuit, or plain toast, first thing in the morning, before getting up, helps to settle the stomach, and it is also well worth avoiding the smell of frying food at that time of day. If this means you have to miss your cooked breakfast, then it is a small price to pay. Eating little and often will help, rather than sticking to the traditional three meals a day. Recent research has suggested that drinking old-fashioned ginger beer helps some women.

If your partner is going through a spell of feeling nauseous at the thought of food, do be considerate about what you eat when you are together. Nibble to your heart's content when you are out of the house or at work, but if your job involves business meetings in restaurants or pubs, do keep quiet about any wonderful meals you have had. Your partner will certainly appreciate it.

FATHERS FEEL IT TOO!

The symptoms of pregnancy aren't only experienced by mothers. It isn't unknown for men to develop cravings too, or to manifest any of the many physical symptoms of stress – such as insomnia, indigestion, nausea and so on. Morning sickness in 'pregnant' men isn't a joke: it can be very real. However, the more you both talk about and share your emotions, the less likely you will be to suffer symptoms of stress.

It is also common for expectant fathers to go through considerable swings of mood, from enthusiasm and optimism to anxiety and despair. In addition, many fathers experience the often unexpected sensation of emotional numbness in the early weeks. At least one in ten of all expectant fathers experience a phenomenon called the couvade – a word derived from the French word *couver*, meaning 'to brood'. The most typical symptoms include: indigestion and heartburn (often aggravated by the anxiety that frequently accompanies pregnancy); constipation; backache; and loss of appetite.

Many of these symptoms are simply related to stress and are not unique to fathers-to-be, of course. Nausea or stomach pains, for example, can be just as common in men who are worried about their work. It has been suggested that men who experience the symptoms of couvade are possibly of a more anxious nature than the average person and in particular seem to have problems coping with the inevitable mood swings, as they oscillate between feelings of confidence and inadequacy. But symptoms like these can at least encourage empathy and sympathy for your partner – no bad thing in itself. As with any stress, sharing problems can help tremendously, so do talk to your partner about how you feel.

FINANCIAL IMPLICATIONS

Having a baby obviously has all manner of implications for the wallet. After the first flush of excitement has faded away, most fathers begin to wonder just how much it is all going to cost. Not only does having a baby cost money – in terms of baby clothes, nappies, cot, carrycot, pram and all the other paraphernalia of parenthood – but there may well be effects on income too.

❝ It was extraordinary. I know I would feel excited, but this really was an incredible feeling. When the pregnancy test came back positive we were both on cloud nine, and nothing else seemed to matter. This was something for just the two of us, something to share, to talk about, and to dream about. And then the anxieties began to creep in. It hadn't really been planned, and I didn't even know if we could afford to live on just one income. Was our flat big enough? Could we possibly cope with a baby? It seemed a dreadful responsibility. ❞

Benefits for expectant and new mothers

▶ Free prescriptions and dental care for all pregnant women.

▶ Statutory Maternity Pay (SMP) – paid for 18 weeks in total, and available to women who have worked for their employers for at least six months without a break into the 15th week before the baby is due (the 26th week of pregnancy), and who earn enough to pay National Insurance Contributions.

▶ Maternity Allowance – paid for a total of up to 18 weeks to women who are not entitled to SMP because they are self-employed, give up work or change jobs during pregnancy.

▶ Sickness Benefit – can be paid to women who don't get SMP or State Maternity Allowance, but who have paid enough National Insurance Contributions in a previous tax year to qualify.

▶ Maternity Payment from the Social Fund – a lump sum available to families on Supplementary Benefit to help pay for the things you need for a baby.

▶ Child Benefit – a tax-free weekly cash benefit paid for each of your children.

Other possible benefits worth enquiring about include One-Parent Benefit, Family Credit, Low Income Benefits, and so on. Free milk and vitamins are also available to mothers on Income Support.

If your partner currently goes out to work, there will be a loss of income if she chooses to give up work to look after your child, or children. At present, men's incomes tend to be higher than women's, and so it is usually the fathers who stay at work after the baby is born. This may be gradually changing. In some areas, high male unemployment means that it is the fathers who look after the children while the mothers go out to work. In other families, parenthood is genuinely shared. But for many families, the mother's paid employment is likely to end – if only temporarily.

The loss of income can put extra pressure on the father at a time of potentially high expense. It can make him work harder than ever, putting in longer and longer hours, to compensate for the lost income, and this can isolate fathers from their families at the very time when they are most needed. Children also tend to arrive at difficult times in a man's career, when promotion is being sought or a position is really being established. If your work is causing you stress like this, ask yourself what you are working for, and whether the hours and money truly compensate for what you might be losing.

You may also need to look carefully at your accommodation. Is it large enough? What might have been ample space for the two of you may seem dreadfully cramped for three, or more. Moving house, whether buying or renting, also has all sorts of financial implications.

With all these potential problems, do ensure that your partner claims all the benefits that are available. The full list is complicated, but is explained in leaflet FP8 'Babies and Benefits', obtainable from any office of the Department of Social Security. Some of the available benefits are listed in the box above. It is vital that you get all the appropriate forms and, if in doubt, apply. You won't get any benefits if you don't ask.

KEEPING HEALTHY

Everyone knows that pregnant women should look after their health. Sensible eating, avoiding smoking, and cutting out alcohol have all been shown to be beneficial to the mother-to-be. However, it really makes sense to ensure that both parents are in the best possible shape. Health and fitness are not just your partner's responsibility.

In recent years there has been an increasing emphasis on the importance of being in good health before conception occurs. Some doctors and midwives run special 'pre-conception clinics' to offer advice, check on nutrition and so on. However, one side-effect of this apparently excellent development may be a tendency by some couples to consider it too late to look after their health once the baby is actually on the way. Nothing could be further from the truth. It is simply never too late to look after your health.

Take smoking, for example. In an ideal world both parents would give up smoking well before pregnancy occurs. However, if you simply haven't been able to do this, don't shrug your shoulders and say 'What's the point? It's too late now.' It isn't. Stopping at any time will help your baby.

If you smoke and your partner does not, there is still a very real risk to the unborn child from passive smoking. And if your partner was a smoker, and has managed to give up for the sake of your child, it really isn't fair for you to continue puffing away. As well as the effects of passive smoking, you are making the effort of stopping much harder for her.

Even if the baby is due tomorrow, it still isn't too late for you both to try and stop – for the baby's sake, not to mention your own. Recent research has clearly shown that babies in households where someone smokes have more infections and other medical problems; in particular, ear and chest infections are more common in families with a smoker. If you have ever suffered from earache, you will know how miserable ear infections can be. You can't possibly wish that on your child, can you? Stop now.

The same goes for alcohol. Since it is advisable for the sake of the baby that a pregnant woman stops drinking, or at least cuts right down on alcohol, it is hardly fair if you sip your wine, beer or spirits every evening while your partner looks on enviously. A little thought and consideration pays dividends. It also goes without saying that all drugs are best avoided during pregnancy; you must check with a doctor first about any medication your partner needs.

TRAVELLING IN PREGNANCY

There is absolutely no reason why you and your partner shouldn't travel wherever and whenever you want in pregnancy. But there is one very real exception. If your partner is feeling sick, then travel of any sort can be horrendous. After all, it is bad enough being sick in the comfort of your own bathroom, but it is countless times worse in a coach speeding up the fast lane of a motorway. If travel is essential when she feels nauseous, then do at least go prepared. An empty plastic ice cream container, with lid, is the perfect receptacle, or you can purchase children's travel sickness bags, identical to the type used on aircraft.

On any long journeys, it is essential that you either have regular stops for your partner to stretch her legs, or else encourage her to move her legs about and wiggle her toes regularly. Even on a plane, she should walk up and down at least once an hour. Pregnant women are more prone to blood clots in the deep calf veins, and keeping the legs still for long periods increases this risk considerably. Clots like these can spread to the lungs and be very dangerous, so prevention is much better than cure.

If you are both travelling abroad any time after 25 weeks, check on the quality of medical care in the country you are visiting. Premature labour is not uncommon, and, if you have any doubts, your partner should ideally stay at home. Air travel is perfectly safe in early pregnancy, but most airlines are reluctant to carry pregnant women after 32 weeks. There is always a risk that she may start into labour, and five miles high in a jumbo jet is hardly the ideal place for childbirth. It also raises all sorts of interesting questions about the nationality of a child born in another country's airspace. It is much better to stay at home late in pregnancy!

SHARING YOUR EMOTIONS

Many men are surprised by their emotions during their partner's pregnancy. After the initial pride and panic, all sorts of other feelings can surface. Most men become intensely protective towards their partner and unborn child. Modern man may not be able to show this by reinforcing the defences around his castle, but instead he may take out insurance policies, start to feel more concerned about the future of the world, and begin to worry about his own, his partner's, and the baby's health. Share such worries with your partner: she may be having the same or similar thoughts, and in any case it helps to talk your anxieties over together.

Many couples find that pregnancy brings them very close together, sharing intimate thoughts and feelings, fears and needs, in a way that never happened before. This closeness can be tremendously important, as the next few months are likely to bring such mixed blessings as sleepless nights, and the hundred and one other stresses that can test any relationship. Building on a close relationship now will pay handsome dividends for you both in the future.

As well as these positive feelings, many men also feel jealous. Some see the developing child as coming between them and their partner, as if the amount of love she has is fixed and must now be shared out between you. Fortunately, love is not a mathematical equation and it is perfectly possible for both of you to love each of your children, and your partner, one hundred per cent.

Finally, most men worry about the unknown. They are far from certain what changes the pregnancy will bring, what will happen to their sex lives, what the labour will be like, and how they will cope with a brand new, helpless human being. The rest of this book will help prepare you, reassure you, and encourage you. And if you still doubt that you can cope, just look at your friends. If they managed, so can you! You have a lot more to offer to the life of your developing child than simply providing the sperm that made it all possible.

Did you know?

It's nothing short of a miracle, if you think about it. An ovum is the size of a grain of sand, and a sperm is microscopically tiny, but put them together and they develop into a perfect human being – your baby. Understanding what is happening from conception to the baby's birth will make pregnancy and childbirth both more fascinating and less worrying.

The womb, or uterus, is where everything happens. While the egg is released by the ovary, and fertilization occurs in the Fallopian tube, the baby grows and develops in the uterus. Before pregnancy, the uterus is only about 5cm by 10cm (2in by 4in) in size, and is the shape of an upside-down pear. It is made of muscle with a small opening at its base, called the cervix, through which blood passes during menstrual periods. In pregnancy, the cervix becomes blocked with a plug of mucus, and this plug stops germs entering the uterus.

Throughout pregnancy the muscle of the uterus grows, thickens and stretches. Even though it starts off so small, and may end up containing a baby weighing 4 kilos (10 pounds), it is quite remarkably strong and flexible and will not split or tear. During labour it is the tightenings, or contractions, of this muscle that eventually lead to the baby being delivered.

The process of fertilization

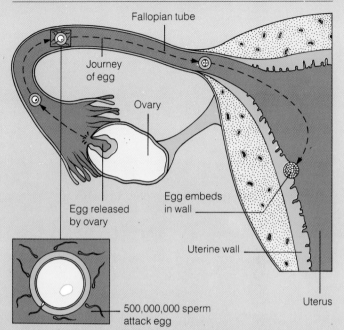

Fallopian tube

Journey
of egg

Ovary

Egg released
by ovary

Egg embeds
in wall

Uterine wall

Uterus

500,000,000 sperm
attack egg

How fertilization occurs
During intercourse up to 400 million sperm are ejaculated into the vagina. A few get through the cervix and swim through the womb into the Fallopian tube. A single sperm joins with the ovum, and from this moment the sex and physical characteristics of the fetus, such as eye colour, are determined. Over the next week the fertilized ovum passes down the tube and finally embeds in the thickened lining of the uterus.

Week 1	Week 2	Week 3	Week 4

Menstruation
Pregnancy is dated from the first day of the last menstrual period. After menstruation, the ovaries produce another ovum, or egg, by the process of ovulation, and this grows in the ovary for the next two weeks. It is then released into the Fallopian tube. If fertilization does not occur, the ovum is shed, along with the womb lining, in the bleeding of the monthly period.

Fertile period
The ovum is only just visible to the naked eye and just after it is released by the ovary, the woman is at her most fertile. Fertilization takes place in the Fallopian tube and only requires a single sperm. The fertilized ovum passes down the tube towards the uterus, dividing over and over again. By the time the ovum reaches the womb it is a mass of over one hundred cells.

Dating the pregnancy
Fertilization usually occurs two weeks after menstruation. When the fetus is two weeks old, four weeks will have passed since the last menstrual period. Since the pregnancy is dated from the last period, rather than conception, at this stage your partner will be described as four weeks pregnant. The average pregnancy lasts for 40 weeks.

THE ROLE OF THE PLACENTA

The placenta, or afterbirth, is vital to the success of the pregnancy. It develops once the fertilized ovum embeds itself in the uterus, and is fixed to the lining. The placenta contains over 100 arteries, and by the end of pregnancy is about 20cm (8in) wide and 2-5cm (1-2in) thick. The baby's blood is pumped by its own heart along the umbilical cord which joins the fetus to the placenta. In the placenta, a very fine membrane keeps the baby's and the mother's blood separate, but allows oxygen, vitamins, glucose and other nutrients to pass through from mother to child, while waste products and carbon dioxide are passed back to the mother. Antibodies also cross to the baby, but so do drugs, nicotine and alcohol.

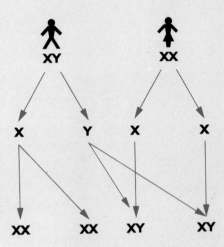

The chromosomes determine a child's sex. Sperm contain either X or Y chromosomes, whilst the ovum contains only X chromosomes. If a sperm with Y chromosomes fertilizes the ovum, the child will be a boy. If it is a sperm carrying the X chromosome, then the child will be a girl.

The baby itself floats gently in fluid, or liquor, in the amniotic sac – a two-layered bag of membranes attached to the placenta. The gentle fetal movements, which start at around seven weeks, are unlikely to be felt by the mother until 18 to 20 weeks. The liquor also protects the baby against bumps and jolts. In the great majority of falls or other injuries, the amniotic fluid disperses the impact, leaving the baby unharmed.

Towards the end of pregnancy the placenta gradually becomes less efficient. If the pregnancy goes on longer than expected, there may come a point at which the doctor considers that the placenta has deteriorated so much that the baby would be safer and better nourished if it were delivered. This is one major reason for induction, or starting labour artificially. Sometimes the baby's growth slows earlier in the pregnancy, because the placenta is functioning less well. Looking for early signs of placental failure is an important reason why your partner has more check-ups towards the end of pregnancy. Problems are more likely in women who have high blood pressure, in older mothers, or if part of the placenta has separated away earlier in pregnancy. This separation usually, though not always, causes slight vaginal bleeding.

The growing fetus

At 16 weeks (right), the pregnancy has usually just begun to show, though this varies from woman to woman and largely depends on the tone of the abdominal muscles. As early as 12 weeks, all the baby's major internal organs are present in their final form and are beginning to function.

At 40 weeks (below), the baby is ready to be born. The average weight of 3kg (7lb) is well over five billion times the weight of the fertilized egg.

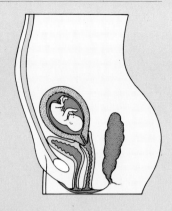

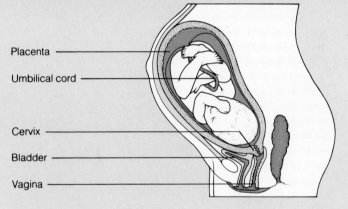

Placenta

Umbilical cord

Cervix

Bladder

Vagina

MISCARRIAGES

Miscarriages are most likely to occur in the first 12 weeks of pregnancy. Indeed, more than one in ten pregnancies ends in this way, and most early miscarriages are due to problems with the fetus or the placenta. They can almost be thought of as nature's 'quality control' mechanism, although this obviously doesn't make them any the less distressing when they happen. In most women, having one or even two miscarriages does not increase the risk of this happening again in a later pregnancy, although occasionally repeated miscarriages may be due to some underlying illness in the mother.

Slight bleeding in pregnancy is not necessarily the first sign of a miscarriage, though it may be termed a 'threatened miscarriage' or 'threatened abortion' by a doctor. The bleeding quite often stops of its own accord, with the pregnancy carrying on perfectly normally. However, if bleeding starts, it is vital that your partner rests immediately and sends for a doctor.

As well as feeling desperately sad after a miscarriage, most couples feel guilty and look for something to blame, particularly making love. In fact there is little evidence that this causes miscarriages. Women who have had previous miscarriages may be advised to avoid intercourse in the first few months – but this is often because it is known that the couple will blame themselves if anything goes wrong. If your doctor does give this advice, remember that there are plenty of ways of making love that don't involve full intercourse.

HOW THE BABY DEVELOPS

The speed of a baby's development over the first weeks and months is nothing short of astonishing.

The first ten weeks

At four weeks the fetus is just visible to the naked eye. By seven weeks it measures 8mm (¼in) from head to bottom, and by 14 weeks it is 56mm (2¼in) long.

The baby's heart and nervous system are beginning to develop at the time of the mother's first missed period, and the heart actually begins to beat at six to seven weeks. When you consider that it may go on beating 70 times a minute for the next hundred years – more than three billion beats! – then you realize what a miracle conception is.

Ten to twenty weeks

As early as 12 weeks, the fetus is fully formed. All the major internal organs are present, and the baby is beginning to move about. By 13 to 14 weeks the heartbeat is strong enough to be detected with an ultrasound detector. Hearing this wonderful sound for the first time is often the moment when parents start to really believe that there is somebody growing inside! If you cannot get to your partner's antenatal clinic, she might be able to make a tape recording of the heartbeat for you to hear later.

Twenty to thirty weeks

By 18 to 20 weeks most mothers begin to feel the baby kicking, and shortly afterwards you will be able to feel this marvellous sensation too. Sometimes you can see the baby wriggling, especially if your partner is lying in a warm bath. The amount that babies kick varies a great deal. Some seem to kick constantly, while others move hardly at all. By 26 weeks the baby's eyelids will separate and open for the first time, and from 28 weeks the child will have a good chance of survival if it is born early. Such premature babies would need intensive nursing in a Special Care Baby Unit, as many organs, particularly the lungs, will not have matured completely.

Thirty to forty weeks

Nowadays a baby born at 32 weeks has more than a 90 per cent chance of survival with good intensive care. However, 85 per cent of all pregnancies end between 38 and 42 weeks, when the mother goes into labour. Don't worry if your baby doesn't turn up on the predicted day: the 'expected date of delivery' is never meant to be more than a rough guide.

The extent to which the pregnancy shows varies greatly. Many women worry that their baby looks too small, or too large. In fact, the amount that the swelling shows depends mainly on the way that the baby is lying, the shape of the mother's waist, and the strength of her abdominal muscles. Some women look huge from a very early stage. Others hardly look pregnant at all, even when they are nearly at full term. Your doctor or midwife will be constantly checking to ensure the baby is growing satisfactorily. It is the size of the baby that matters, not the size of the lump!

Development of the fetus

12 weeks The fetus is fully formed and moving about. It now has to mature.

20 weeks Your baby is growing quickly, and you will soon be feeling movements.

24 weeks Your baby has developed a pattern for waking and sleeping, and now responds to noise.

28 weeks The baby's eyelids are now open and the eyes almost always blue. She will be kicking hard.

32 weeks By now, the baby is usually lying head first, ready for birth. The lanugo hair begins to disappear.

40 weeks Any time now! The baby is fully matured, and ready for the great adventure of life.

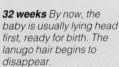

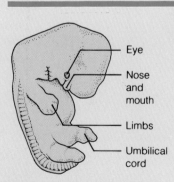

Eye

Nose and mouth

Limbs

Umbilical cord

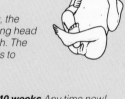

Actual size of hand at 8 weeks

20 weeks

6-week fetus (above) The heart has begun to beat, there are dimples where the ears will form, and buds for the limbs.
Development of the hand (right) Fingers begin to form at 6 weeks and at 11 weeks the fingernail beds have developed.

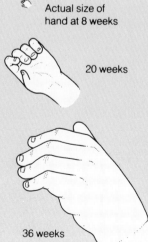

36 weeks

The three stages of labour

In the first stage of labour the cervix gradually opens, or dilates (a). This stage usually lasts 6-12 hours in a first pregnancy, though subsequent pregnancies may be quicker. The womb contracts repeatedly, and this slowly reduces the length of the cervix. The central canal of the cervix then gradually opens (b). At the start of labour this canal may be just 1cm (½in) wide but it slowly enlarges, typically at a rate of 1 cm (½in) per hour. When the cervix is around 10cm (4in wide), and large enough for the baby to pass through, the second stage starts (c).

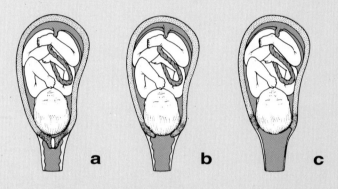

a   b   c

GOING INTO LABOUR

On average, babies are born 280 days from the first day of the last period, though an irregular menstrual cycle can make this calculation less precise. Towards the end of her pregnancy your partner will notice early signs that labour is not far away. The baby tends to kick less, the mother may lose a little weight, and contractions increase. Throughout pregnancy, the womb contracts repeatedly, and in the last few weeks these tightenings become more frequent and more noticeable, although they remain quite painless. The actual onset of labour is usually obvious from one of three signs:

A 'show' At the start of labour the mucus plug from the neck of the womb often comes free, and is passed out of the vagina. There is usually a little blood mixed with the mucus.

Regular contractions The contractions of the womb become stronger and more frequent. When they are coming at a rate of one every 10–15 minutes, your partner has almost certainly started in labour.

The waters break The bag of amniotic fluid sometimes breaks right at the start of labour, or this may not happen until labour is well under way. It may be felt as a slight trickle down the leg, or a torrential gush!

Once labour has begun, it is divided into three stages, as shown above. The cervix opens up in the first stage, the baby is born in the second, and the placenta is delivered in the third. The baby herself doesn't have to do anything at all during labour. Every time there is a contraction she is moved down the birth canal by a few millimetres, and slips back slightly between contractions. Progress may seem slow, but this is the last lap.

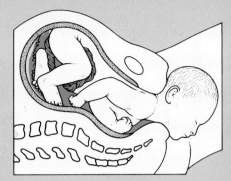

During the second stage of labour, the end is at last in sight. The mother's pushing assists the contractions of the uterus and the baby is finally born.

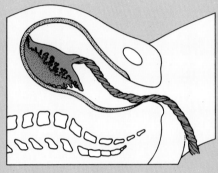

In the third stage, the placenta is delivered. This usually happens about 10-15 minutes after the baby is born, and the mother will only need to give a very gentle push to expel it.

GLOSSARY

Below are some medical terms you may hear used by doctors, or come across in books concerned with pregnancy.

Abortion: Medical term for 'miscarriage' – a pregnancy ending before 28 weeks.

Amniotic sac: The bag of membranes inside the womb which contains the fluid in which the baby floats.

Braxton Hicks contractions: The contractions of the uterus which are felt throughout pregnancy.

Cervix: The neck of the womb.

Ectopic pregnancy: A pregnancy that gets stuck in the Fallopian tube instead of passing to the uterus. This cannot develop normally, may be dangerous, and needs to be removed surgically.

E.D.D: Expected Date of Delivery.

Embryo: The developing baby in the first ten weeks.

Lanugo: Fine hair which covers the baby from 22 weeks until just before birth.

Liquor: The fluid that surrounds the baby in the uterus.

L.M.P: Last Menstrual Period.

Obstetrics: Branch of medicine dealing with pregnancy and childbirth.

Ovum: The egg produced each month by the ovaries, about the size of this full stop.

Placenta: The afterbirth.

Premature labour: Labour starting before 37 weeks.

Primigravida: A woman having her first baby.

Term: The end of pregnancy.

Uterus: The womb.

Vernix: A protective white greasy substance that covers the baby's skin in the last few weeks before birth.

Getting involved

You're in this together. The more involvement you have in the pregnancy the better for you, your partner and the baby. But it isn't always easy. Many men find the first weeks and months very confusing – they might be enthusiastic about becoming fathers, but simply can't face the world of antenatal clinics and classes. Don't worry if you feel this way. Take your time – but try to avoid treating pregnancy as a departing train that you board at the very last minute!

From a practical point of view, try to help more around the house right from the start: don't wait to be asked. If your partner is feeling tired and sick, then extra help will be more than appreciated. But both of you need to beware the 'Catch 22' whereby helping is seen as a criticism of her ability, and not helping is seen as male chauvinism. You should also both accept that your standards may be very different!

WHERE WILL WE HAVE THE BABY?

Early on in the pregnancy, a decision must be made about the best place to have the baby. The huge majority of births in the U.K. take place in hospital, but in some areas home deliveries are becoming more common. Home births can be wonderful, naturally full of joy and warmth. They can also be nightmares. The advantage of hospitals is that specialist equipment and expertise is instantly available if it is needed – their disadvantage can be that technology can swamp humanity. It need not, however, and many hospitals have improved out of all recognition in recent years.

Home is rarely the best place for the birth of a first child as there are so many unknown factors. But if a first delivery was normal, and you are not too far from specialist care, home may well be ideal for subsequent children. Your doctor or midwife will advise you on this.

However, the decision is not simply home or hospital. In your area there may be a choice of hospitals, with different ways of doing things. There are consultant specialist units, and hospitals where your partner can be cared for by your G.P. and community midwife. Some hospitals offer a five-day stay, others offer two days or less, even down to the splendid DOMINO (Domiciliary-In-Out) system, in which the mother is mainly looked after by her midwife and G.P. The midwife goes to hospital with her, performs the delivery and, if all is well, mother and baby go home six hours later, after which the midwife will continue to visit and support you all.

Finding out

The decision on where your child should be born must be reached together. Get hold of as much information as you can, talk it over with friends, and share your feelings. But in the end, you must support the choice your partner makes, because she will have the labour, and the final choice should be hers. Decisions on pain-relief techniques should also be shared, but again the buck stops with the mother-to-be.

Your partner's G.P. should be an expert on the local facilities and can make arrangements. Information is also available from:

▶ Your community midwife
▶ Your local health visitor
▶ The head of midwifery services in your district (look in the phone book under your local Health District)
▶ The Community Health Council
▶ The National Childbirth Trust (see Useful Addresses, page 62)

ANTENATAL CLASSES

Antenatal classes may be run by your local hospital, community midwife, health visitors or the National Childbirth Trust. Your partner can find out early in pregnancy what is available in your area. Most antenatal classes positively encourage fathers to attend and they are invited to every class. In other areas special fathers' classes are held in the evening, particularly when the usual classes are in the daytime.

The classes usually cover topics such as health, relaxation techniques, labour, childbirth, pain relief and childcare. Such classes also give you a chance to meet other parents, and fathers often find great relief in discovering that other men are experiencing exactly the same emotions as they are.

Do approach these classes with an open mind. If you are too rigid, deciding from the start that – for instance – you want the birth to be as 'natural' as possible, then this may not necessarily be in your partner's best interests. Certainly have preferences, but be prepared to modify them as the pregnancy progresses. For reasons completely out of your hands, the best-laid plans may fail and you may both be left feeling disappointed and disillusioned unless you have learned to be flexible.

ANTENATAL CARE

Wherever the baby is to be born, your partner will need to attend an antenatal clinic. This may be at the hospital, at your G.P.'s surgery or the local Health Centre. Various check-ups – such as your partner's weight and blood pressure and the baby's size – are routinely performed, and are recorded on a record card or chart similar to the one illustrated below.

Fathers should always feel free to go along to the clinic with their partners, though the times are often inconvenient. Nevertheless, if you want to go – do ask. Many doctors, particularly family doctors, are delighted to see the father and to answer any questions he has, and to demonstrate the baby's heartbeat and so on.

In some antenatal clinics your partner may experience a long wait for what seems to be a very short appointment. While this may seem infuriating and unacceptable, do all you can to encourage her to keep attending. It takes just a minute to record her blood pressure, for example, but early detection of high blood pressure can literally save the pregnancy. It really is worth the time and effort.

How an antenatal record card works

Height of fundus
This records how much the womb has grown and compares it to the expected growth. The height of the fundus (top of the womb) should therefore correspond approximately to the number of weeks your partner is pregnant at each visit.

Position
Various abbreviations are used to describe which way the baby is lying – facing sideways, frontwards or backwards.

DATE	WEEKS	HEIGHT OF FUNDUS	WEIGHT	PRESENTATION ENGAGEMENT	POSITION	REMARKS
18.6.90	12+	12	52.5	⟋	⟋	Ultrasound
16/7/90	16	15	54.25	⟋	⟋	All well
13.8.90	20	20	55.5	ceph	⟋	
10/9/90	24	23	56.75	ceph	—	Progressing w

Presentation
This indicates which way up the baby is lying in the womb. Up to 30 weeks the baby keeps changing position, but then usually settles down to lying in a head down position. This is written as 'Ceph' or 'C' (cephalic) or 'Vx' (vertex). Bottom down is 'Br' (breech).

Engagement
The head engages when its widest part passes into the pelvis. 2/5 means two-fifths of the head can be felt.

THE RECORD CARD

Different hospitals and doctors use various types of card or form to record the details of the pregnancy. In some areas your partner will be given her complete set of hospital records, but usually she will be given a record card, known as a co-operation card, like the one illustrated here. The records allow all the doctors and midwives involved in looking after your partner's pregnancy to know exactly what is happening at any time. It could be disastrous if part of the team did not know what the other part had discovered or was planning.

When your partner comes home from the clinic, read the antenatal notes together, and if either of you don't understand anything in them, ask! It's your baby, not the hospital's. And since the stories about doctors' handwriting are often true, if possible your partner should check that she can read the card before leaving the clinic!

It is essential that your partner takes her record card with her wherever she goes. It contains all the information that any doctor or midwife might need, should she go into labour prematurely or need medical attention for any other reason.

B.P.
The blood pressure is normally below 140/90, and tends to stay fairly constant. A rise in the final weeks can be harmful and is monitored closely.

F.H.
'FHH' means fetal heart heard; R shows it is regular. 'FHNH' means fetal heart not heard (before Week 12, or due to the baby's lie).

Urine
This is tested for protein and glucose at every visit. 'NAD' means it is normal. '+' or 'Tr' means a trace of one of these has been detected.

appointment	BP	Hb	FH	OEDEMA	URINE	NEXT VISIT	SIG
	125/65	✓	✓	nil	NAD	GP4	PC
	130/65	✓	✓	nil	NAD	4/52	CJ
	120/65	✓	✓	nil	NAD	4/52	PC
	120/60	✓	H	nil	NAD	4/52	CJ

Hb
''Hb', or haemoglobin, is mainly a measure of iron in the mother's blood. A low value may indicate a need for supplements.

Oedema
Oedema (swelling of ankles, feet or hands) may occasionally be an early sign of pre-eclampsia (see Glossary, page 53).

Next visit
Appointments are usually every 4 weeks until 28 weeks, then every 2 weeks until 36 weeks, then every week until the birth.

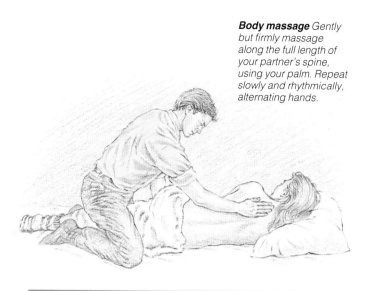

Body massage *Gently
but firmly massage
along the full length of
your partner's spine,
using your palm. Repeat
slowly and rhythmically,
alternating hands.*

MASSAGE IN PREGNANCY

Massage? In a book for expectant fathers. Whatever next? In
fact, massage can be a wonderful way of helping your partner
during pregnancy, so if you have never attempted massage
before, do give it a try. Giving each other a body massage can
be tender and relaxing, intensely pleasurable and deeply
erotic, while enabling you to feel comfortable and familiar with
the changes in your partner's body.

Towards the end of pregnancy, especially when full
intercourse can sometimes become awkward or
uncomfortable, body massage can give very considerable
sexual pleasure. However, massage is not just a sexual activity.
It can be a marvellous form of relaxation, good for both of you
when the stresses are building up. It can also play an important
role in the first stages of labour, bringing relief from your
partner's painful contractions.

Finally, massaging your partner's abdomen will not only feel
pleasurable to her, but also makes very real contact between
you and your baby. You feel the movements as the baby kicks,
and since there is plenty of evidence that babies can hear in the
womb, your child will begin to relate to your voice and your
touch at an early stage.

Important guidlines for massage

■ Be firm enough: massage that is too gentle can sometimes
feel like a tickle. Using the palm of the hand is more effective
than the fingers. All massage should be smooth, firm and
rhythmical. Using oil or body lotion will allow your hands to slide
comfortably over the skin.

■ Before you start, ask your partner what she enjoys. Not
everyone likes a total body massage, so find out what parts of
her body she likes having touched and start there. She may find
it easier to demonstrate on you than to explain in words.

■ Make sure you are both in comfortable positions, and in a
warm room, from the start. Take your time, and don't hurry.

Massage for relaxation

There are countless ways that you can massage each other for relaxation, and pregnancy is the ideal time to learn a habit that can last you the rest of your lives. When massaging for relaxation, always take it slowly. Going too fast is anything but relaxing. As well as stroking, gentle kneading and circular rubbing can be extremely effective. For a start, try the two simple techniques illustrated on these pages. For a body massage, your partner should lie on her side. And for a neck and shoulder massage, she can either lie flat on her stomach, or sit astride a chair, facing its back, and leaning on a pillow or a large cushion.

Massage for labour

Since the natural response to any pain is to attempt to rub it better, gentle massage during labour can certainly lessen your partner's pain as well as helping her to relax between contractions. Massage in labour can be very valuable. The physical contact also binds you closely together during this highly emotional time. Massage is most effective in the early stages of labour, but towards the end simple touch or hand-holding will help your partner to feel calm and confident.

To successfully bring relief from pain, massage for labour needs to be practised beforehand. Useful techniques for labour include abdominal massage and thigh massage, both illustrated on the following pages. Back massage, in which circular pressure is applied to the small of your partner's back, also gives relief during contractions.

Neck and shoulder massage
First massage the base of your partner's neck, then gently apply pressure to the base of her skull. Return to the base of her neck, massaging either side of the spine, then stroke her upper arms from shoulder to elbow.

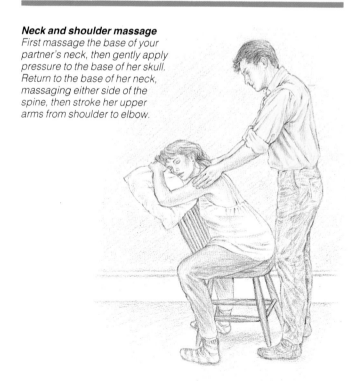

RELAXATION TECHNIQUES

For most people, pregnancy is the time when they first learn about relaxation techniques. These are widely taught in antenatal classes and both mothers and fathers frequently find them of use years later when faced with other types of stress.

During any form of stress, your muscles tighten. Just feel your muscles next time you are tense: the chances are the muscles of your back, arms, jaw and many other areas will be rigid and tense. Try letting them go – the tension eases instantly. But few people can let their muscles relax at will, without training.

In pregnancy, simple relaxation exercises help to teach awareness of one's body as well as improving the circulation, and preparing the muscles for the second stage of labour. Practise them together regularly during pregnancy, taking turns, and find the positions that you think can best be adapted for use during labour, to ease the pains between contractions.

Your partner should get into a really comfortable position. Speaking slowly and calmly, ask her to think about her toes and ankles, to wiggle them about, then let them drop absolutely loose. You then work up the body, encouraging her to tighten and then relax each group of muscles in turn. Go from the feet to the ankles, then to the thighs, bottom, spine, neck, scalp, forehead, cheeks, teeth and jaws, shoulders, arms and finally the fingers. At the end, just let her lie there quietly for a few minutes. The sense of relaxation can be total. It's your turn next!

CONTROLLED BREATHING

Breathing comes naturally, doesn't it? Your partner thought so too, until the last weeks of pregnancy, when the growing baby wriggling under her ribs starts to make breathing more difficult. It is normal for mothers at this stage to need occasional deep breaths and sighs. And during the hard work of labour she will need even bigger breaths.

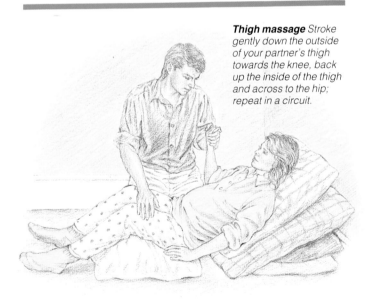

Thigh massage Stroke gently down the outside of your partner's thigh towards the knee, back up the inside of the thigh and across to the hip; repeat in a circuit.

Abdominal massage
Using a light touch and
both hands, massage in
a figure-of-eight
movement across the
lower abdomen. This will
help to ease painful
contractions.

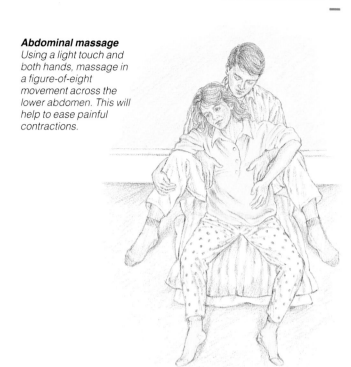

It is important that pregnant women learn to control their breathing so that it is calm, unhurried and efficient in labour. Whenever people are anxious they breathe more rapidly, and the tension and excitement of childbirth makes this hyperventilation all too common. Rapid breathing is not only less efficient, but it can also cause feelings of muzziness, headache, and even pins and needles, resulting from an imbalance of oxygen and carbon dioxide in the blood. The natural reaction to pain is to tense the muscles and hold the breath; if your partner does this often in labour, she will tire.

One of the reasons you should learn the breathing techniques too is that during labour your partner may well need help and guidance to recall precisely what should be done. The excitement, pain and feeling of panic may make the lessons slip her mind. It is most important that you encourage your partner to practise her breathing exercises regularly.

Controlled breathing for contractions

▶ Gently blow a breath out as each contraction starts.
▶ Breathe in slowly through the nose, trying to fill the lungs as fully as possible, then let the air out through the mouth with a gentle puff.
▶ While breathing out, try to release the build-up of tension, and in between contractions relax every muscle.

PRACTICAL PROCEDURES

Throughout pregnancy, various tests and other checks may be offered to your partner. If either of you don't understand why something is being suggested, then ask. The more you understand, the less worried you will be. The commonest tests that may be offered are listed below.

The ultrasound scan, which in most units is now carried out routinely at about 16 weeks, is done to measure the baby and to exclude the possibility of twins and certain major abnormalities (see illustration below).

Alpha-fetoprotein measurement tests for AFP, a chemical in the mother's blood that occurs in much higher concentrations if spina bifida is present. However, this test is not always totally accurate, and sometimes high levels are detected with no abnormality. AFP testing is therefore used as a screening test: if it is positive, further examinations will be carried out. It is not yet available everywhere.

Amniocentesis is usually offered to mothers over 35 to detect major fetal abnormalities such as Down's syndrome or spina bifida. A needle is passed through the abdominal wall into the uterus, and a small sample of amniotic fluid is taken and examined. This test can be extremely valuable, but there is no point in having it if your partner would choose not to have a termination if something was found to be wrong. The test itself carries just over a one per cent risk of triggering a miscarriage. Make sure you both fully understand the implications of an amniocentesis before it is carried out.

Chorionic Villus sampling, though not yet available everywhere, is an accurate test offered to women at high risk of having babies with genetic abnormalities. A fine tube is passed through the cervix, and a sample of chorion (tissue which contains fetal cells) is taken and examined. Performed at around eight to eleven weeks, it allows the option of an early termination if required.

PAIN RELIEF

In modern obstetrics there are many possible options for pain relief (analgesia) and you should find out about them all. However, you should both beware of taking up extreme views. For instance, some people believe that if a woman does not

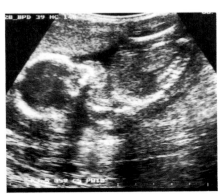

Having an ultrasound scan

Your partner's abdomen is smeared with a jelly before the scanning machine is passed over it. The picture of your baby appears immediately on a television screen. Though indistinct, it is usually possible to identify the baby's head, backbone and limbs.

undergo the full experience of labour, this diminishes the event and she won't appreciate her child fully later on. This is simply nonsense, with no evidence to support it whatsoever. Others see the use of analgesia as failure, believing that there is something noble about going through childbirth without any drugs. The same could be said of going to the dentist!

What is important is that the woman should make the decisions, aided by the father-to-be, and not have them forced on her by the medical profession. It is your job to ensure that your partner has been fully consulted, understands the pros and cons of what she is being offered, and is reaching her decision without pressure.

The main possibilities include:

Natural methods: the techniques learned in pregnancy, such as relaxation, massage and breathing.

Gas and air: a mixture of nitrous oxide and oxygen. Your partner can hold a mask and control the rate at which she breathes this in. It takes only 15 to 20 seconds to work, so is ideal during contractions. There are few side-effects, but if used too much, gas and air can make her sleepy.

Injections: the commonest pain-relieving drug is pethidine, which takes about 15 minutes to work and lasts for two hours or more. Though effective, it may make your partner feel sick or rather sleepy.

Epidural injection: though not available everywhere, it is highly effective. An anaesthetist puts a needle into the space between the vertebrae in the lower spine, and inserts a fine plastic tube through which local anaesthetic can be given regularly. It is usually effective within 20 minutes and should give total pain relief for two or three hours, and can be topped up as the effect wears off. Its effectiveness can paradoxically cause one real disadvantage, in that it may take away the sensation of contractions, making it harder to know when to push. Some mothers find the lack of all sensation wonderful; others find that it diminishes the experience of childbirth.

General anaesthetic: may have to be used if a Caesarean Section is performed, and very occasionally for a complex forceps delivery. Some hospitals will carry out a Caesarean under an epidural.

WHO'S WHO IN ANTENATAL CARE?

The midwife: midwives may be based either in hospital or in the community. They are nurses who have received extra training not only in delivering babies, but also in caring for mothers and babies throughout pregnancy, labour and the postnatal period.

The obstetrician: a consultant obstetrician is a hospital doctor who specializes in looking after pregnant women, and who heads a team of more junior doctors.

Your G.P.: most G.P.s offer obstetric care. Some provide only antenatal and postnatal care, shared with the hospital specialists, while others also care for mothers during childbirth.

The health visitor: Health visitors are nurses who have had extra training in caring for people, particularly small children, in the community. A midwife will visit your home daily up to ten days after the baby is born, after which the health visitor takes over.

Can it harm the baby?

As one father put it to me so very memorably, 'It just didn't seem right making love with someone else there, even if the someone was my own unborn baby!'

He wasn't the first father-to-be to feel uneasy, or embarrassed, or even frightened about the subject of sex during pregnancy. Very many couples have doubts, fears and questions about this important aspect of their relationship. In this chapter I shall be looking at some of the reasons for these fears and problems, and offering practical advice to help you both have an enjoyably sexy pregnancy.

After all, no-one would deny that the physical and sexual side of your relationship is vitally important at all times, including pregnancy. At such a crucial time in your lives, you both need ways of expressing your love, affection and concern for each other. Sex is more than just an adult form of playtime: it is the ultimate expression of sharing and caring. However, make no mistake about it – your relationship is bound to be in for a few changes over the next few weeks and months.

EMOTIONAL CHANGES

To begin with, the changes in the hormones circulating in your partner's body will inevitably affect the way she feels during pregnancy. Most men are already well used to the emotional changes that many women go through just before their monthly periods. Many women even feel that they are like a 'Jekyll and Hyde' personality, swinging from being placid and reasonable to acting like a fire-breathing dragon, quite dramatically and for no apparent reason.

Exactly the same sort of changes occur in pregnancy. Moodiness is one of the cardinal signs and symptoms of pregnancy. You will find that your partner is at times happy, enthusiastic, optimistic and really looking forward to having the baby. On other occasions the world will seem a far bleaker place. She will feel sad, pessimistic and may even have profound feelings of regret about being pregnant at all.

Understanding the reasons for all these mood swings is obviously important, particularly as it is quite likely that your partner will take out her frustrations, tension and regrets on her nearest and dearest – in other words, you! If she does, bite your tongue and realize that she almost certainly doesn't mean it. Of course, if she says the same to you whatever mood she is in, then she probably does mean it – and that is quite another story!

The emotional upsets are never quite straightforward either. If your partner has a day of feeling down and unenthusiastic about pregnancy, then this is likely to be accompanied or followed by feelings of guilt about not being 'maternal'. Listen, really listen, to these worries, and reassure her that such feelings are very common. But remember: reassurance without understanding is never effective.

Most fathers also have mood upsets. Becoming an expectant father makes most men feel very protective and keen to provide every material need for their partner and child. They may work longer and longer hours to earn as much as possible, and then spend their spare time decorating the house and doing all the D.I.Y. jobs that are needed to make the home completely ready for the baby. In addition, many men feel that their partners are already burdened with quite enough problems, and tend not to share their own anxieties. Sadly, a few couples begin to drift apart at the very time that they should be feeling closer.

With the potential for fears, upsets and insecurities like these, a close and loving physical relationship is all the more important. And in fact pregnancy can be the time when many couples find that their sex lives improve quite remarkably.

PREGNANCY AND SEXUALITY

There are no simple rules about how pregnancy will affect sexuality. For instance, many couples find the whole experience enhances their feelings and sexual interest. The joy of becoming parents, the feelings of love and caring that they share, and the freedom from both menstrual periods and the need for contraception can help many relationships. Other couples experience the very opposite, with a reduction in sexual interest and desire by one or both partners.

Even when a woman is not pregnant, changes in libido, or sexual interest, are really very common. For most of us, libido varies from day to day and week to week. However, in pregnancy such changes are even more marked, both in women and their sexual partners. The hormonal changes associated with pregnancy can wreak havoc with libido, and it is very common for women to lose interest in sex at the start of pregnancy. In addition, many pregnant women see themselves as unattractive and anything but sexy, and this affects their whole self-image and self-esteem. Finally, morning sickness and the exhaustion that many women feel at the start of pregnancy can curtail a vigorous sex life.

> **" I think my wife was more concerned and bothered about her appearance than I was. To me it really didn't matter that she was nearly two stone heavier and walked with a waddle. She still looked beautiful to me and was carrying my baby. That was all that mattered. She began to get self-conscious about my seeing her naked, and got upset when her breasts started leaking milk. I had to keep reassuring her that I still found her attractive and still wanted to make love. "**

If a women's libido is reduced, this can trigger off feelings of frustration and even jealousy in the husband. The jealousy or resentment is often directed towards the unborn child for interfering with their physical relationship.

However, many men feel that their own libido is reduced. Some men worry that intercourse might trigger off miscarriage or labour, or might possibly damage the baby, and they can feel inhibited by the presence of the unborn child, even at the very earliest stage of a pregnancy.

Reduced libido is not an inevitable problem, or one that will not come to an end. In fact, many couples reach the end of pregnancy with their sexual relationship heightened and improved. Problems do tend to be temporary. As at other times of stress, such as moving house or changing a job, there are bound to be repercussions on your sexuality. You can't leap into bed and suddenly make all the cares and concerns of the world disappear. But there is no denying that it is a very good place to gain some relief from them.

WHAT IS SAFE?

Many couples have very real fears about the safety of intercourse, but in general almost all sexual activities are perfectly safe throughout pregnancy. There is, however, one golden rule: be gentle and be considerate.

In some cases, doctors do advise against intercourse in the first three months of pregnancy, but for most couples there is no need for this at all. If your partner has had miscarriages early in pregnancy in the past, or has had any bleeding in this pregnancy at all, then you should certainly discuss this question with your doctor. There may well be reasons for avoiding actual intercourse, but – as we shall see – that need not put an end to an enjoyable physical sexual relationship.

However, provided you are considerate, then there will be few problems. For instance, most women find that their breasts are very tender at the start of pregnancy. If you choose this time to caress them enthusiastically, then don't be too surprised if your partner doesn't share your enthusiasm! Similarly, at the end of pregnancy the breasts can again become quite tender, and begin to secrete colostrum – a milky substance that is produced before the milk itself comes in. Be gentle and thoughtful and you will run into few problems.

The first three months

At the beginning of pregnancy two very common symptoms that are experienced by most expectant mothers can have considerable implications for your love life. Almost all women feel very tired in the first few weeks. Whether or not this is simply nature's way of making the mother take things easy I am far from certain, but it does mean that bedtime gets too precious for sex. Bedtime is for sleeping! Don't be surprised if your partner falls asleep in a chair in the early evening, wakes a few hours later, struggles up to bed, and falls asleep almost straight away. She's not trying to tell you anything except the fact that she's tired! Women who go out to work, or have other children to look after in the home, tend to get particularly exhausted.

The other common and well-known symptom is morning sickness. For many sexually enthusiastic young couples, the morning is an ideal time to make love. But not when you feel sick, it isn't. The answer to both the tiredness and the nausea can be a simple one: don't forget the afternoons and the early evenings. These can be ideal times to make love, especially at the weekends, and can really rejuvenate your sex lives.

At the same time, it is equally important to remember that there is more to sex and the physical expression of love than just intercourse. If your partner is feeling exhausted, nauseous, and possibly anxious, intercourse may well be the last thing she wants. Far better to cuddle, caress, and hold her, possibly adapting and using some of the massaging techniques described in the last chapter. Telling her that massage and cuddling is all that you intend to do can sometimes be a great help. She may be very keen to be cuddled, but at the same time worried that if she shows too much enthusiasm then you will end up having intercourse – which she may not want. A mutually agreed innocent and loving cuddle may be the physical affection that you both need at some of the more tricky phases of pregnancy.

The middle three months

By the middle of pregnancy, most women tend to feel much more energetic again. The nausea and tiredness have faded, and the lump is not yet too ungainly. Indeed, many women feel a quite marked increase in their libido during these months. There is some evidence that the increased blood flow to the vaginal area increases sexual arousal, makes orgasm more easily reached, and increases lubrication. Enjoy yourselves.

“ I really found it difficult to fancy Susan when she was pregnant, especially towards the end of the pregnancy. I tried to keep my feelings to myself, but sometimes it was difficult to feel aroused when she wanted to make love. I didn't love her any the less, but I simply couldn't get used to seeing her so large. Fortunately, everything eventually got back to normal after the baby was born. ”

The final three months

From a physical point of view, the increasing size of the baby poses all manner of challenges to lovemaking. In addition, both you and your partner will inevitably be growing more anxious about the approaching birth, and this is bound to have an effect on your interest in sex.

A pregnant woman's changing shape and size upsets some men, while exciting others. If you do feel uncomfortable about your partner's size, please don't joke about it. She is bound to be feeling very self-conscious about being so 'fat', and teasing remarks, even if made in fun, can be hurtful. In fact, nothing can be more feminine than a woman in advanced pregnancy. However, if you do not find her swelling abdomen sexy or attractive, there are bound to be other physical aspects of her that you can praise and compliment her about. Even at the end of pregnancy, a little flattery and courtship does no harm!

WHICH POSITIONS ARE BEST?

In the early weeks and months of pregnancy, there is no reason why you should not use any position for sexual intercourse that you both choose. It is probably wise to avoid those positions that involve deep penetration, but if you follow the rule about being gentle and considerate then this won't be a problem.

However, in the later months of pregnancy many common positions become less satisfactory. You will need to try different positions and find out what is comfortable for your partner, and what suits both of you. Some women find that positions with the man on top can aggravate backache and cause them to feel dizzy, as well as being physically almost impossible when the baby has reached a large size. You may find positions in which you both lie on your sides much better for making love in the later stages of pregnancy.

Do experiment. For a great many couples, pregnancy is the time when they discover greater sexual awareness and intimacy, which will give them pleasure for the rest of their lives.

What about orgasm?

Particularly at the end of pregnancy, many couples worry that female orgasm might set off labour prematurely. If this was the case, then doctors would not have needed to invent all the other forms of inducing labour that are sometimes required! The answer would be simple and fun.

There is, however, some evidence that orgasm can trigger off a temporary increase in the Braxton-Hicks contractions that are normal throughout pregnancy, and it seems probable that an orgasm can possibly trigger off labour in women whose pregnancy has gone well past the expected date of delivery. If you are in that position, so to speak, there is no harm in trying. There are worse ways to spend the time that you are waiting!

INTERCOURSE ISN'T EVERYTHING

Pregnancy is an ideal time for rediscovering the fact that you can have a splendid and satisfying sex life without having full intercourse. If your partner's doctor has advised against intercourse, for reasons mentioned earlier in this chapter, or if pregnancy has reached a stage where intercourse is simply too uncomfortable, then try to recall the many other ways of making

" Before Jill became pregnant we had an extremely active sex life. Then, during those first few weeks and months, she had the most dreadful nausea and sickness and everything ground to a halt. I found it more than a little frustrating, but I love her and understood how she felt. As she began to feel better, our sex life changed a lot. We spent longer cuddling and stroking each other. We had intercourse less often, but I think we felt closer and more loving in those months than we ever had before. "

love. Sex should be fun, so don't forget all the enjoyable ways of using your bodies to show your love and affection, and to give each other sexual pleasure when the pregnancy makes straightforward intercourse difficult.

On a hygiene note, you should bear in mind that vaginal lubrication tends to be not only much greater during pregnancy, but also to have a more pronounced odour. If this causes problems, then both of you could bath or shower before making love.

In conclusion, never forget that there is much much more to sex than intercourse, however satisfying that might be. Sex is really only one part of physical affection. Just holding each other, cuddling on the sofa as you watch television, or going to sleep in each other's arms, are all vitally important parts of your physical relationship.

Pregnancy can bring couples even closer together.

Being prepared

As the months of pregnancy pass, your thoughts will inevitably turn towards preparing yourselves and your home, in readiness for the new baby. It is no good waiting until the last minute to organize everything. You need to think out ahead what is needed, not only in terms of getting the baby's room ready, and choosing and buying major items of baby equipment, but also in terms of making financial and legal provisions for your family. You will also need to start thinking about a checklist of things to do in connection with the big day itself, and to prepare yourself mentally for anything that could go wrong at the last minute. It doesn't matter who does the particular tasks required, as long as they get done. Parenthood is for sharing, and so are the jobs that come with being a parent.

THE COST OF PARENTHOOD

Every now and again you will read articles on how much it costs to have children. These figures are usually horrifying, and act as a highly efficient contraceptive! If you start by adding up the capital outlay on a cot, nappies, toys, baby clothes and so on, and then add to this the loss of your partner's earnings, the overall reduction in your family's disposable income can seem very substantial on paper, though it is partly compensated for by the various benefits listed in the first chapter. However, in reality most people find that in the early years children can be remarkably cheap to run, and few doubt that it really is worth it!

Some of the larger items of furniture and equipment, such as cots and prams, may well be bought as presents by enthusiastic grandparents, saving you from a huge initial outlay. And enough baby clothes to last most of the first year are often presented as gifts by friends and relatives when the baby is born, in addition to soft toys and accessories for the baby's room. Most couples with a new baby will also be offered all manner of hand-me-down clothes, toys and babycare equipment. Don't be too proud to accept these. After all, they won't have been worn or used very much, for the simple reason that babies grow so quickly.

If you do buy expensive essentials, like cots and pushchairs, brand new, then do look after them carefully. When your children no longer have any use for them, you should have little or no trouble in finding a buyer. Most childcare clinics have noticeboards where parents advertise their sales and wants.

In addition, remember that your expenditure on social activities will inevitably lessen towards the end of pregnancy. You are far more likely to spend evenings together at home than to go out dancing the night away! When the baby arrives, you will also discover the fun of trying to find a babysitter: this alone tends to make you cut down on those spontaneous evenings out, and thereby saves the expense that these usually involve. Although few new parents resent these changes to their lifestyle, please don't abandon going out completely, whatever you do. Parents need to recharge their batteries too!

INSURING FOR THE FUTURE

An important aspect of financial planning has to be insurance. Once your income is having to support not just yourself, but also your partner and child, you really do have to consider what would happen if for some reason you were unable to work. Even more drastically, your responsibilities now extend beyond the grave – if you were to be killed in a road accident tomorrow, who would support your family?

You cannot, of course, predict what may never happen, but you can at least take out sufficient insurance cover to protect your family. Discuss the whole subject with your partner and then with a reputable independent financial advisor (most of them are members of F.I.M.B.R.A.).

An insurance adviser will also be able to help you with arranging some form of financial provision for your child, should you wish to consider this. In fact, if you put a birth announcement in the paper there is a high chance that you will be inundated with leaflets and policies! But it is far better to talk it over with an expert and you will find it well worth considering some form of endowment policy on your child's life. This will put aside a set amount should he or she die, but more usefully it will provide a lump sum of cash at the end of the policy, typically at 18 years of age. Though that may now seem a long way off, the money will come in remarkably useful, whatever your child chooses to do at that important age.

This is also a very good time to consider making a will. Yes, you – at your age! Just think the unthinkable for a moment. After the baby is born, if anything were to happen to you and your partner, what would become of your child? Who would look after him? Determining who should be your child's legal guardian is tremendously important, so do discuss this with your partner. Even though the chances are extremely remote that anyone will ever need to see your will before the time your child reaches adulthood, talk it over with a solicitor soon. A little effort can gain immense peace of mind.

PLANNING A NURSERY

The nesting instinct is universal: everyone wants to get their home just right in time for the baby's birth, and in the weeks and months before the baby is born you and your partner will spend many hours making practical plans for his arrival. Getting everything ready is an important part of preparation for parenthood and many expectant fathers tackle the business of designing, decorating and generally preparing a nursery for the child with great enthusiasm. It is one very practical way in which they can show how much they want to care for the baby.

Where will the baby sleep?

Don't feel guilty if you haven't the space for your baby to have a room of his own initially; he can perfectly well sleep in your room for the first few months. In every other species, babies sleep with their parents. Indeed, sleeping apart is a relatively new development in the human race, and is still primarily a Western phenomenon. Throughout the world, even today, more women sleep with their babies than with their partner. Many Western parents also find that bedsharing with their child is both practical and successful. It is certainly completely safe, provided that you and your partner do not take sleeping tablets or drink alcohol before bedtime. Both of these can interfere with the reflex that prevents parents rolling on top of the child.

When deciding on a room for the baby's eventual nursery, don't make the common mistake of choosing and decorating a spare room that turns out to be in the coldest part of the house, or you will soon notice the increase in your fuel bills. It is important that you keep the baby's room heated in cold weather and a thermostat on a heater will help maintain a constant temperature of about 20 °C (68 °F).

ESSENTIAL EQUIPMENT

Almost every expectant father is staggered by the amount of equipment a baby seems to need. If you are not careful, it is all too easy to get carried away and feel that you must purchase everything right at the start. But a baby's immediate needs are

Finishing touches

Mobile

Wall frieze

Nursery lamp

Stencil motif

The baby's nursery

Make sure there is a sturdy, flat surface on which to change your baby's nappies. A plastic changing mat with raised sides will prevent a young baby from rolling off.

If you are going to bath your young baby in the nursery, use a baby bath on a purpose-made stand, and don't fill it too full. Make sure that the room is adequately heated.

A low, comfortable chair enables you or your partner to feed the baby in the nursery. Make sure you can both easily get in and out of the chair with a baby in your arms.

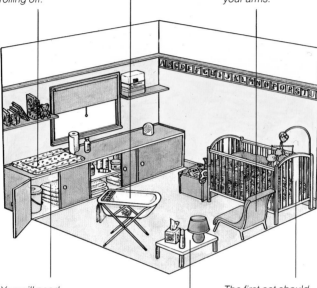

You will need adequate storage for the baby's clothes and other requirements. Nappies and toiletries should be readily to hand when the baby is being changed.

A sturdy, low table should be placed close to the chair, so that tissues and other useful items can be kept within reach. A low-wattage table lamp facilitates night feeds.

The first cot should have high sides, a safe dropside mechanism and, above all, should be robust. If it is placed in a corner, it will help the baby to feel more secure initially.

actually very simple – somewhere to sleep, a supply of clothes and nappies, and something to be carried about in. You can assess the other requirements after the baby is born and purchase them at different stages, as they become necessary. You need only provide special nursery furniture and decoration if you enjoy these yourselves. Babies don't care about the surroundings in which they sleep and are nursed, as long as they are warm and comfortable.

In contrast, some parents feel that it is tempting fate to buy anything at all before the baby is actually born. This attitude is very understandable, and in fact many stores will allow you to reserve nursery items, such as prams and cots, and will only charge for and deliver them after the birth.

Cots and carrycots

While you can put your baby in a full-size cot right from the start, he will feel safer and more secure in a smaller cradle or carrycot for the first two or three months. A carrycot will allow you to transport the baby easily, not only from room to room, but also to friends and relatives when you want to go out, and a carrycot on wheels will make an ideal pram. Always make sure that the base is stable, and that it cannot tilt to one side. If in doubt, stand the carrycot on the floor, well out of people's way (unless you have underfloor heating, in which case the carrycot should be on a proper stand).

Wicker cradles or Moses baskets can be a very attractive first bed, and are also suitable for carrying your baby about. However, make sure that the inside is not rough; it should preferably be fully lined. Some cheaper baskets carry a real risk of scratching the baby. Carrycots and baskets have the advantage of sides which protect your newborn baby against draughts, although you can use 'cot bumpers' to pad the inside of larger cots to the same purpose.

A carrycot or basket is fine until your baby is about eight weeks old, but is not really safe once he can roll over. By this time a cot will be required. When choosing a cot, make sure it conforms to British Standards for Safety (no. BS 1753). There must be adequate safety catches to prevent the dropside falling down accidentally, high sides and ends to stop a baby climbing out, and specified minimum spaces between the bars.

Prams and pushchairs

An increasing number of families get by with a sling for carrying the baby around indoors, and with a carrycot on wheels – and then a pushchair – for outdoor use. If you do decide to buy a pram, your choice will depend partly on how much space you have to keep it in and whether it needs to be collapsible for journeys. Above all, make sure that a pram is safe (it should conform to BS 4139): it must be stable so that it cannot tip, however hard it is rocked. A pram should also be easy to push and manoeuvre, and the brake both completely secure and easy to use. Every design has advantages and disadvantages and you will have to weigh these up, for your own requirements.

There are safety standards governing pushchairs (BS 4792). It is important for most families' lifestyle that a pushchair folds, and some models have a 'lie-back' position as well as forward- and backward-facing positions to suit different ages.

BUYING SECONDHAND

If you buy any baby equipment secondhand, do scrutinize the safety aspects carefully, since the original model may not have been covered by safety regulations introduced recently. For instance, ensure that a cot hasn't been repainted with paint that could contain lead, that it has no splinters, and that the bars are close enough together to prevent a baby getting his head stuck between them. Check that prams and pushchairs are sturdy, with no loose nuts or bolts, and that their brakes work perfectly. Remember, safety is a thousand times more important than appearance. There are certain safety items that you will want to buy and install to make your house more childproof, and some of these are illustrated on the opposite page.

Making your home safe

The nursery Make sure a baby's room is safe and secure, with soft flooring and no sharp edges anywhere. Install a baby alarm to enable you to hear your baby crying when you are in another room.

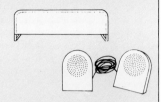

The bathroom Store medicines in a childproof cabinet. A non-slip bath mat will prevent a small child from slipping, but a baby should always be held.

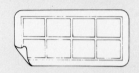

Stairs A wall-mounted smoke detector will sound an alarm if a fire starts. Use a safety gate once your baby starts crawling, until he can negotiate the stairs.

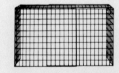

The kitchen This can be the most hazardous room in the house for children. Curly flex on a kettle and other electrical equipment prevents a young child pulling things down from the worktop. Cooker and hob guards can protect a child from burning himself.

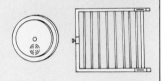

The sitting room All types of fire must be protected by an appropriate fireguard, but you should also never leave a child unattended in a room with a fire.

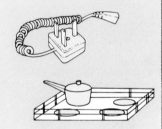

Safety around the house As your baby grows, and becomes more mobile, new hazards continually present themselves. Child-resistant catches can be fitted to drawers or cupboards that do not lock, and socket covers will prevent a child poking objects, or his fingers, into empty electric sockets. Fix safety film to glazed doors or windows within a child's reach.

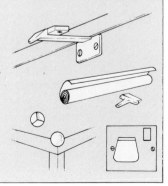

COUNTDOWN TO D-DAY

As the big day approaches, it is essential that you are as prepared and well organized as possible. Some panic is inevitable, but planning ahead certainly makes life much easier. Even though I had just finished six months working in a maternity hospital, and had delivered well over a hundred babies, I still flew into a blind panic when my wife went into labour with our first child. If you draw up lists and schedules, and display them in a prominent place, you will at least feel as if you know what you are doing.

Try to get organized by at least a couple of weeks before the expected date of delivery. If you wait until the last minute, you are bound to forget something. Also, don't forget that babies are human, and like most humans they are rarely punctual. The expected date of delivery that you were given is really only a guide, at best an approximation, and your baby could well be either early or late. So be prepared two weeks before the date, and, on the other hand, don't panic if the date comes and goes, and the baby doesn't arrive.

Countdown checklist

▶ Make a note of the hospital's telephone number, and the numbers of your midwife, doctor and the local ambulance service. Put a copy of this list by the telephone. Keep a copy in your wallet too, and make sure you have some coins or a Phonecard for public telephones – in case anything happens when you are both out together.

▶ Make sure your partner knows how to contact you all times.

▶ If this is not your first child, ensure that arrangements have been made for someone to look after your other child or children when you set off for the hospital. If he is old enough, tell your child what is going on, so that he realizes he isn't being abandoned.

▶ If you are going to hospital by car, make sure it is running well and that there is plenty of petrol in the tank.

▶ Make a list of the names and telephone numbers of everyone that you will need to call from the hospital with the good news: your parents, her parents, close friends, favourite aunts, and so on. Put the list where you won't forget it.

▶ Although your partner will have packed her case in readiness for the day she goes into labour, you should also think about what you will need to take to hospital. Pack up your own bag beforehand, as far as possible, and include some or all of the items listed on the opposite page.

HOW DO WE KNOW IT'S LABOUR?

There are three main signs that it is time to go to hospital at the end of pregnancy (see page 18). If any of these happen, don't delay – go right away.

▶ The water (amniotic fluid) breaks or leaks;

▶ Vaginal bleeding or a 'show';

▶ Regular contractions occuring every 10-15 minutes for a first baby.

For subsequent children your partner will almost certainly know when she is in labour. Believe her! And don't worry about false alarms. No-one will mind if you arrive at the hospital and everything seems to fizzle out. It is much better to be safe than sorry. And if you are in any doubt about whether your partner *is* in labour, then don't hesitate to call your midwife or speak to someone at the delivery unit.

GOING TO HOSPITAL

Make sure you wear something cool and loose as maternity units are notoriously hot. Many men dress in clothes that are far too warm and feel distinctly uncomfortable and light-headed as the tension and excitement build up. You don't want to be fainting from overheating at a critical moment – the midwives have quite enough to do! Collect your partner's hospital bag, add any last-minute items to your own, notify anybody you need to that you are off to hospital – and leave!

You probably do not need to worry too much about the hospital stay itself, since your partner will have packed some baby clothes, nappies and baby toiletries if these were not being provided by the hospital. In fact, many hospitals do provide nappies and creams etc. and also like to keep babies in hospital clothes while they are there. Your partner will have an opportunity to ask you to bring in anything else she needs, or has forgotten, when you visit each day.

However, you should concern yourself with baby clothes and any equipment that will be needed when it is time for your partner and baby to come home, such as the carrycot and warm outer clothing.

Father's bag

▶ Snacks and nibbles to eat (fruit, nuts or chocolate may keep you going during a long night's labour – but aren't recommended for your partner, even though she will be doing all the work!).

▶ A personal stereo and two sets of headphones with cassettes of favourite music.

▶ A good book for each of you to read if the night gets really long, particularly if your partner is having an epidural.

▶ Crosswords or playing cards if playing together would help pass the time, and help your partner to relax.

▶ A camera to take those unrepeatable pictures straight after the birth.

▶ A supply of coins or a Phonecard for the public telephone box.

▶ Body lotion or oil if you are going to practise some of the massage techniques described earlier.

COPING WHEN THINGS GO WRONG

However well planned a pregnancy might be, however carefully you both look after your health, and however much high quality antenatal care your partner may receive, there are still occasional emergencies and tragedies at the end of it all. Every parent starts to worry, especially towards the end of the pregnancy, that their child may be stillborn, handicapped or deformed, or abnormal in any one of a thousand ways.

How would you cope if things did go wrong? No-one can know for certain, but it is sensible, rather than morbid or depressing, for you both to talk about your fears before the baby arrives. You will find it comforting to worry together, rather than alone, and you should certainly share any fears with your doctor or midwife.

Stillbirth

Perhaps the saddest event of all is a stillbirth, the term used for a baby born dead after the 28th week of the pregnancy. The chances of your child being stillborn are very small; however, current statistics reveal that one in 200 births are stillbirths.

The prevention of a stillbirth is probably the single most important aim of antenatal care. Nowadays it is frequently possible to detect a distress in a fetus well *before* it dies, and to deliver it prematurely. The earliest sign of fetal distress is usually a reduction in the baby's movements, and if your partner notices a significant change in these, it is vital that she reports this to her doctor or midwife straight away. Usually there will be no problem, but occasionally more detailed tests will reveal whether the baby is going to be safer left in the uterus, or should be delivered and cared for in a Special Care Baby Unit (see page 51).

In many cases of stillbirth, fetal death is in fact confirmed before the baby is delivered. Since it is obviously extremely distressing for the mother to know that she is carrying a dead child, induction is almost always carried out as soon as possible after the death has been confirmed.

If a child is stillborn, the parents' initial reaction is bound to be one of stunned disbelief, grief and shock. But many men, in particular, find the open expression of grief difficult or embarrassing. If it happens to you, try not to suppress the sadness you feel; it is much better to express your feelings. Don't worry that your tears will upset your partner and make things worse for her. Weeping together can actually be a strengthening experience for you both.

If possible, try to see and even hold your baby. If you can obtain a photograph, this too will help your grieving process. The loss of a stillborn baby is as much a bereavement as any other, since you have by then had a real relationship with your child for several months.

More than anything, you will want to know why the stillbirth occurred. A post mortem may shed light on this, but in some cases doctors are still unable to provide an answer. It is important that you understand as much as possible, and this may also dispel some of the guilt and anger that so many parents unnecessarily feel. It will also help to talk to other parents who have lost a child in this way, so do contact the support group (see Useful Addresses, page 62).

EMERGENCY CHILDBIRTH

It *can* happen. For any one of a number of reasons, you just might not make it to the hospital in time. That has set you panicking, hasn't it? In fact, emergency childbirth without the help of a doctor or midwife is a relatively rare event. If you both follow all the instructions about when to go to hospital, and don't try to wait at home until the last minute, it is extremely unlikely to happen to you either.

That is one reason to stop panicking. The other is the realization that nature is remarkably clever. Every species manages perfectly well most of the time, and *if* an emergency happened, the chances are that you would both cope as well. Most births happen entirely normally without – or despite – skilled help, and only in a small minority of cases does skilled help make that essential difference.

So, in the unlikely event of you having to deliver your child alone, how are you going to cope when your partner starts going into labour and tells you in no uncertain fashion that she can definitely feel the baby coming?

▶ Stop panicking, and start to act decisively.

▶ Ask someone to telephone for a doctor, midwife or ambulance.

▶ Wash your hands.

▶ Tell your partner to lie down, if possible on a towel, and remove the bottom half of her clothing.

▶ Encourage her to pant, with shallow breaths, rather than to push, to slow down the birth.

▶ The baby will probably appear very quickly. Hold him with his head very slightly down until he cries; this way he is less likely to inhale fluid. He will be extremely wet and slippery.

▶ Congratulate your partner and tell her the baby's sex. Gently dry the baby with a clean cloth or towel, and wrap him in another clean towel for warmth.

▶ Lie him on your partner's abdomen so that he doesn't get cold.

▶ If possible, tie the umbilical cord with wide cord or ribbon; string or cotton is no use as it may cut through the cord.

▶ The contractions will continue until the placenta delivers. When it does, simply tie the cord once more. The baby can stay attached to the placenta until a midwife or doctor cuts the cord.

▶ Get your breath back. If a doctor or midwife has still not arrived, call them again. Someone will need to check the baby thoroughly and attend to any stitching that is needed.

Congratulations – you did it! Breathe a deep sigh of relief . . . and vow to get to the hospital a bit earlier next time.

D-day

The big day has arrived at last. You've made it to the hospital, and at some time in the next 24 hours you are going to become a father. All those months of antenatal classes, of talking, thinking and planning are now reaching a climax. That well-known cliché, 'Today is the first day of the rest of your life' is more true today than ever: nothing will be the same again.

The more that you understand about what is happening, the more you will get out of the powerful experience of childbirth. The classic image of the expectant father, pacing nervously up and down a hospital waiting room until a midwife puts her head round the door and says 'It's a boy!', depicts someone who is only on the periphery of one of the major events in his life. Expectations of a father's role have changed so much that now you are quite likely to feel under pressure to be present during the labour, even if you don't want to be. However, some men simply do not want to attend, others are unable to be there, and some women would rather not have their partner with them. If this is the case, I would urge you to bear in mind two things. First, a woman should not be alone during labour. If you cannot be there, it is important that she has a close companion with her throughout the experience. Secondly, there is no reason to think that your bonding and relationship with the baby will be damaged in any way if you are not there at her birth.

WHAT CAN YOU DO TO HELP?

Just being with your partner throughout this emotional experience can be almost enough in itself. It is well known that fear worsens pain, and childbirth is inevitably going to be a time of considerable anxiety, but your steadying influence, in holding her hand and talking calmly, will give her great support.

The hospital staff will involve both of you in their explanations and instructions. Try to avoid making comments or asking questions that may alarm your partner, but at the same time you may be able to help her understand certain procedures, and you can also ask questions on her behalf if she is in the middle of a contraction.

At the start of labour, your chief role is simply to keep your partner company. She may stay in bed, she may wander about the unit. Either way, there may be quite a long spell during which little seems to be happening. Later on, when labour is well under way, she will certainly not be interested in conversation. That doesn't mean that your presence won't be a help, but your partner will be concentrating on coping with her contractions. You may find that she suddenly starts to take all her frustrations out on you when she is experiencing serious pain. She almost certainly won't remember her comments later; it would be tactful if you forgot them as well!

Towards the end of the first stage of labour, many women experience a sudden outpouring of emotions. She may weep, feel unable to cope, and start to use language that you never thought she knew. Be warned: this is a common experience, and one that rapidly passes once the second stage starts.

Practical help during labour

As labour starts, your first reaction may well be one of relative helplessness. All around you are hospital staff to whom this is second nature, bustling around efficiently. You may feel totally out of your depth – but there is much you can do to help.

Your supporting role

■ Remind your partner to use her breathing exercises. If you learned them too, do them with her, before the pain intensifies.
■ Be positive. Tell your partner that every contraction that she experiences is one fewer – and a step nearer the baby.
■ Encourage her to cope with the contractions one by one, rather than worrying about how long it is all going to take.
■ When your partner says that she really cannot take any more, reassure her that this feeling of desperation is near universal and usuallly means that the end is nearly in sight.
■ Do support your partner's requests for pain relief, and beware of criticism. It's her pain, not yours!
■ Help her to use her gas and air machine. If pain relief does not seem to be effective, tell the midwife.
■ Hold her hand, and let her squeeze yours during contractions.

❝ I was terrified that I would be more hindrance than help. I felt dreadfully nervous about the whole experience, and worried that my panicking would upset my wife. In the end it turned out far better than I ever expected. Watching films of childbirth always made me queasy, but the real thing was much easier. Perhaps it was being so closely involved. It was all so fascinating. I could sit down throughout, which helped, and the midwife said I could go out and stretch my legs and get fresh air if I needed. But I didn't. I felt so immensely proud! ❞

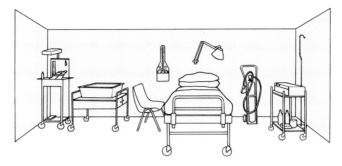

Delivery room layout (from left to right)
Basic resuscitation equipment for the baby (with oxygen); see-through cot (often nicknamed the 'fish tank'); chair for the weary father; bed for the hard-working *mother; 'gas and air' machine (entonox cylinder) for pain relief during labour; delivery pack and other equipment, including fetal heart monitor (CTG machine).*

Using massage

Use the various techniques described on pages 24 and 25; they are very simple, and very effective. In the latter stages of labour, pains that your partner will have been feeling in her lower abdomen may appear to spread through to her back. Many women obtain pain relief through firm massage of the lower spine, especially towards the end of the first stage of labour when the contractions are at their most intense.

As each contraction starts, push hard against the sacrum (the bone at the junction of the spine and the pelvis). If she is lying on her side, it is easiest to stand behind her and press against her back with both hands. Alternatively, you can stand in front of your partner, put your hands around her, and pull against the sacrum.

The later stages of labour

This is when the father-to-be really comes into his own. There is little time to go, but a great deal is suddenly happening.

■ When your partner feels that she wants to push, it is usually a sign that the cervix is nearly fully dilated, so make sure that a midwife knows straight away. Try to persuade her not to push until the midwife has examined her; pushing too early can cause problems.

■ If your partner cannot stop herself pushing, get her to 'huff and puff', which she will have been taught about in classes. It is almost impossible to push if you can't hold your breath.

■ Once she is in the second stage, there is rarely more than an hour to go. When the midwife tells your partner to push down, encourage her to push for a long time during each contraction. The length is more important than the power of each push.

■ During the contractions, remind your partner to keep her chin down, which in turn encourages her to push correctly.

■ During the second stage, your commentary can provide great encouragement – particularly on that magical moment when you see your baby's head appear.

■ Between contractions, your partner may well feel exhausted. Wipe her face with a cool flannel, and give her sips of water.

■ Finally, congratulate your partner when it is all over, and enjoy that first cuddle with your newborn child.

PROBLEMS DURING LABOUR

However good the antenatal care may have been, problems can still arise during labour. Sometimes these will have been predicted beforehand, as when a baby is noted to be in a breech position, but half the problems that arise during labour *cannot* be predicted. You should try and understand the different measures or techniques that may have to be used if there are complications.

Episiotomy

This minor operative technique (illustrated overleaf) is commonly used if it becomes apparent that the skin and muscle are likely to tear when the baby's head is delivered. It involves injecting local anaesthetic and then making a small incision in the woman's perineum, the skin and muscle between the anus and vagina. This is usually performed as the head is 'crowning' and eases the delivery. Though tearing is common in nature, a smooth cut tends to heal more easily. After the delivery, the doctor or midwife will stitch the edges of the incision together again.

Forceps delivery

Forceps deliveries are performed under one of four circumstances: if the baby is lying awkwardly or becoming distressed; if the mother is exhausted and finds it hard to push; if the contractions are too weak; or if a woman who has had an epidural anaesthetic finds it hard to coordinate her pushes, because she cannot feel contractions.

Simply being with your partner during labour gives her tremendous support. Holding her in a calm and confident manner can be most reassuring.

The forceps delivery gently lifts the baby from the birth canal. It is *not* used where the baby is stuck. The forceps themselves are shaped like metal salad servers, and act to protect the baby's head during the delivery, although occasionally a 'ventouse', or vacuum extractor, is used instead. An episiotomy (see below) will need to be performed, and some form of local anaesthesia is always used.

Sometimes the doctor may ask you to leave if there is going to be a forceps delivery. If you would prefer to stay, please do ask; your partner will certainly appreciate it.

Caesarean Section

A Caesarean Section is the delivery of the baby by cutting through the abdomen into the womb. There may be several reasons for performing a Caesarean Section, and the main ones include the following:

▶ If the baby is too large to pass safely through the mother's pelvis.

▶ If there are other causes of obstruction of the birth canal, such as *placenta praevia* (when the placenta is lying over the cervix).

▶ If the baby is lying in an impossible position, such as transversely, or in some types of breech presentation.

▶ If distress in the fetus or mother is detected.

▶ If the mother has a medical condition, such as high blood pressure, which may make a prolonged vaginal delivery potentially dangerous for her.

In many cases you will know in advance that your partner will need a Caesarean Section and you will have had a chance to discuss whether you wish to be present or not. On other occasions the operation may need to be performed as an emergency, particularly for fetal distress. This can become necessary for any mother at almost any time in labour and it is important that you both know what is involved and are mentally prepared. Don't worry about being squeamish – you will not see the actual incision, as sterile sheets are draped over her abdomen and a screen positioned over the upper chest.

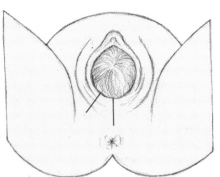

Episiotomy *The incision is usually made at an angle of about 45 degrees, from the centre of the vaginal opening towards one side of the anus. Occasionally, the cut may be aimed more directly towards the anus.*

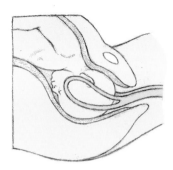

Use of forceps *The commonest reason for using forceps is delay in the second stage of labour. A local anaesthetic is given before they are applied, and the doctor will pull on them very gently. The blades help to protect the baby's head, though an episiotomy will almost always be needed for comfort, and to allow more room.*

The operation may be conducted under epidural anaesthesia, with your partner fully conscious, or else under a general anaesthetic. In this latter case you will almost certainly see and hold your baby before your partner does. But she will want you to remember all the details of the birth.

As with any operation, it will take your partner several days to get over a Caesarean Section. This means longer in hospital, and inevitably some degree of post-operative pain; she will feel sore for some time, but do keep encouraging her.

THE SPECIAL CARE BABY UNIT

It is not uncommon for babies to have to go to the Special Care Unit soon after birth. These can be worrying and alarming places for parents. I well remember the total panic I felt when my daughter was admitted to such a unit shortly after her birth because her temperature had dropped rather dramatically.

The Unit will be full of high technology equipment, drips, bleeping electronic machinery, and some of the tiniest, most frail babies you will ever see. However, just going to the Unit does not necessarily mean that there is anything seriously wrong with your baby. Admission is often a precaution which keeps her under close observation for a while. The staff in Special Care Units are well used to dealing with worried parents. Don't feel stupid if you don't recognize your baby – they all tend to look the same in incubators! Do ask what all the equipment does: once you know what each piece of apparatus is for, your imagination won't run riot.

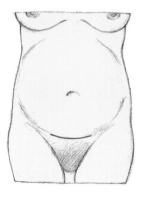

Caesarean incision *The commonest incision nowadays is the 'bikini cut', made crosswise just on the edge of the pubic-hair line. It leaves a virtually invisible scar, and heals well. This low incision takes slightly longer than the 'up and down' incision used in the past and may not be used in an emergency when speed of delivery is a major priority.*

Don't be anxious that your baby will come to psychological harm from being separated from her parents so soon after birth: there is no evidence that this will upset long-term bonding. However, many mothers do feel that they have failed if they see that their child will only thrive with skilled medical and nursing care. Added to this are the problems of getting to know the baby in the difficult and unnatural environment of a Special Care Baby Unit. It is usual for parents' anxiety to last until well after getting the baby home.

PREMATURE BABIES

One of the greatest strides in medical care in recent years has been the remarkable improvement in both the survival and health of those babies that are born either too small or too soon. The phrase 'small for dates' simply means that a baby is smaller than one would have predicted for the duration of the pregnancy; premature babies are those born before 37 weeks.

If your baby is is born too small or too early this is bound to be something of a shock. You probably won't be ready either emotionally or practically, and the little scrap of humanity that you see in the cot is unlikely to match up to your fantasies of what your child would look like. The baby may well need intense nursing care, and you may feel like an onlooker rather than a parent. Your partner is particularly likely to be distressed, and she may feel inadequate, guilty and even jealous of the nurses.

What is certain is that your partner and child really do need you at a time like this. Don't run away into the security of going back to work, pretending that there is nothing you can do. And remember that you will almost certainly look back on this stage of your child's life with gratitude for all that the staff did, astonishment that you ever managed to cope, and delight in how well your child has done ever since.

Now the waiting is over – you are a father. Your baby has arrived, and a new life has begun. If the last few months were fascinating – they were only the start. Enjoy yourselves!

GLOSSARY OF LABOUR AND CHILDBIRTH

Below are some terms that you will hear used by midwives and doctors during labour and childbirth.

Afterbirth: The placenta and the membranes, delivered in the third stage of labour.

Anaesthetic: A drug or procedure which should remove pain. Only a general anaesthetic makes the patient unconscious.

Analgesic: A drug which reduces pain. Morphine or pethidine are the most common.

Breech delivery: This occurs when the baby presents bottom first, rather than head first. The delivery is usually longer, more complicated, and may require a Caesarean Section.

Crowning: The appearance of baby's head from the vagina.

Dilatation: The opening of the cervix during the first stage of labour. The baby is ready to be born when the cervix reaches 'full dilatation'.

Engagement: The baby's head is said to be engaged when its widest diameter has passed the brim of the mother's pelvis.

Episiotomy: The cutting of the *Perineum* to ease the delivery of the baby's head.

Fetal distress: This occurs if the baby is reacting adversely to contractions or labour. It is usually detected by changes in the baby's heartbeat, and the medical staff will act quickly.

Fetal monitors: These detect and measure the baby's heartbeat and/or breathing.

Gas and air: A mixture of nitrous oxide and oxygen that the mother can administer to herself to ease labour pains.

Induction: Starting the labour artificially, either by using medication to stimulate it, or else by rupturing the membranes through the cervix. Only performed when it would be safer for the labour to start.

Lithotomy stirrups: In some forms of delivery, especially with forceps, the mother needs her legs held high and the most comfortable and efficient way is in these special stirrups.

Lochia: The continued loss of blood, discharge and other material of pregnancy from the vagina, in the weeks following the delivery.

Meconium: The baby's first, usually green-coloured, bowel movement. If this occurs into the liquor before the baby is born, it may be a sign of *Fetal distress*.

Oedema: Swelling of the ankles. Very common, but if severe may be associated with *Pre-eclampsia*.

Perineum: The area of muscle and skin that separates the anus and the vagina.

Placenta praevia: A condition in which the placenta may lie partially or completely over the cervix. This can obviously cause problems, and may require a Caesarean Section. Most types are, however, relatively trouble-free.

Posterior position: If the fetus has its backbone curled against the mother's spine, this can cause delay and difficulties in labour. Many babies shift just in time.

Pre-eclampsia: A combination of raised blood pressure, *Oedema*, and protein in the urine. If severe, it can cause harm to the baby, and even lead to the mother having fits. It is always screened for and treated rapidly.

Ventouse: A vacuum-based form of forceps. A suction cup is applied to the baby's head, and gentle traction is then applied.

Now you're a father

It's all over and it's all beginning. The first three months after your first baby is born sees perhaps the greatest change in your lives so far. It is both a wonderful and worrying time, a mixture of climax and anticlimax.

Unless your baby was born at home, you will almost certainly spend much of the first few days visiting the hospital. This is always a very tricky period, since hospitals have a routine and organization that is very different to everyday life. All visitors tend to feel out of place in a hospital, and you are even less likely to feel at home in a postnatal ward full of women and babies.

While maternity leave is now a widely accepted concept, paternity leave is much less common. Nevertheless, most men manage to take some time off work after the baby is born. Don't make the mistake of looking on this as a holiday, with the added bonus of a newborn baby. It will be hard work. It is also probably best to take most of the time off once your partner gets home, rather than while she is in hospital.

If you do decide to carry on working until your partner returns home, the five days or so of hospitalization will be extremely busy. In addition to your work, you will also be visiting your family in hospital, preparing meals and doing some housework at home, not to mention getting everything ready for the great homecoming. There may be baby clothes and equipment to buy, deliveries to arrange, and possibly the finishing touches to be applied to the nursery. In the midst of all this, don't forget to buy your partner a present. It may only be flowers or chocolates but a sign of your love and gratitude will be much appreciated.

MIXED EMOTIONS

Some parents enjoy parenthood right away, finding the whole process easy, natural and satisfying. They love their child from the start and never have a second thought. However, this is far from universal. Many parents, both mothers and fathers, find it hard to feel immediate love for the helpless little bundle that is handed to them. Though this is not at all uncommon, such parents inevitably feel intensely guilty about their lack of maternal or paternal feelings.

It is quite impossible to predict in advance just how you will feel: after all, you have just met your baby for the first time. However, almost always, the first weeks and months see the development of love, affection and warmth. But don't be upset or surprised if you feel little at the very beginning.

This experience is probably more common after the birth of second and subsequent children. While having a first child is usually an intensely exciting experience, second children can often be something of an anticlimax. After all, you and your partner have done it all before; you've been through the traumas of pregnancy and childbirth together, and one newborn baby can seem very like another. I remember a strong feeling of anticlimax after the birth of our son. Our daughter was by then two years old, and although I was thrilled to have a son, I found it hard to feel anything emotionally for this new member of the family. It was only as his personality developed over the next few months that he became a real, individual and lovable person to me. I thought I was unique in this lack of feeling until I talked to other fathers, and found that many of them had felt the same. So don't be surprised if this happens to you.

COPING WITH VISITORS

Your partner and baby are bound to have many visitors, both in hospital and when they return home, and they can be a mixed blessing. This is a very exciting time for everyone and grandparents, friends and relatives will naturally all want to come and admire the new baby. This can prove very tiring, particularly as each and every one will want a full description of the happy event, and will want to give their own comments and words of encouragement.

This doesn't mean that visitors cannot be enjoyed and valued, but it can sometimes all be too much for your poor partner, who has been through an exhausting experience and now has the pleasure of learning first-hand all about feeding, nappy changing and the other joys of parenthood. Since most visitors will speak to you first, and arrange through you when to call, it will be up to you to ask them not too stay too long and to ensure that you leave reasonably long visitor-free spells in the day. Though there will come a time, in a week or two, when much of the excitement will have died down and your partner will really appreciate company, there usually needs to be some restriction during the time in hospital and the first days at home. With tact, and without seeming ungrateful or obstructive, you should be able to prevent too many visitors being a burden for your partner. The worst visitors turn up and expect to be entertained with cups of tea and coffee. The best come for a short time and offer to help out in some way, such as doing half an hour's ironing.

Holding your baby

1 *Slide your hand underneath a young baby's neck and head when picking her up. Support her back carefully with the other hand.*

2 *Always hold your baby close to your body, as this will help her to feel more secure. Again, support her neck with your hand, so that her head cannot roll back.*

FATIGUE AND EXHAUSTION

Having a baby is very hard work. Almost every new mother is genuinely surprised by how tired she feels. The tiredness doesn't last only during the days in hospital, but also carries on during the first weeks at home. Many women expect to be able to come home and immediately take over doing the housework and other chores, as well as caring for the baby. In fact, few of them find they can actually do this. For most new mothers, plenty of rest is absolutely essential. This means a sleep during the day if at all possible, not just ten minutes sitting on the sofa with a cup of coffee. Rest is far more important than the housework, and there is someone else who can do much of the housework – and that is you! In most relationships there is still gross inequality of labour when it comes to housework, and this subject is a common source of friction between couples. If resentment is building up, do discuss it with your partner.

The other way that fathers can help is by pointing out, and accepting, that rest and health are more important than a spotlessly tidy house, perfectly ironed shirts, and meals that are on time. Accept that life has changed. Otherwise your partner may feel intensely guilty about the situation, and struggle on trying to do everything. This will only make her even more tired and lead to a vicious circle. The baby may react to this tiredness and tension by settling less well when cuddled, and by disturbed sleep patterns – which is a perfect recipe for yet more tiredness. Babies recognize when their parents are tired and tense because they sense the physical tension in the muscles of the arms holding them as they are being cuddled.

Changing a nappy

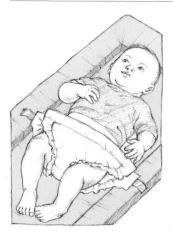

1 Having wiped and dried the nappy area thoroughly, lift your baby's legs gently and slide under the clean disposable, with the tape side of the nappy under her bottom.

2 Pull the front of the nappy up snugly, so that it fits closely round the top of the baby's legs, and fasten the tapes securely at the hips. Make sure that elasticated legs do not chafe.

The secret is for your partner to get plenty of rest, as well as support and help from you. And time will also play its part – tiredness is exacerbated by the hormonal changes in your partner's body, and these will adjust over the next few weeks and settle back to normal.

POSTNATAL DEPRESSION

The 'baby blues' are almost universal, usually occurring on the third or fourth day after delivery. The mother feels emotional, tearful, empty and depressed. There are all sorts of reasons for these feelings, including psychological and hormonal explanations, and usually the depression fades fairly rapidly. Listen to your partner, reassure and hold her during this period – but, whatever you do, don't tell her to 'pull herself together'. Few phrases in the English language are quite as unhelpful as this, and it will be the last thing your partner wants to hear.

Occasionally the 'baby blues' develops into something much more serious. Full-blown postnatal depression is a serious psychiatric illness in which the mother may become acutely and severely disturbed, unable to cope with the baby or even with apparently simple aspects of everyday life. Early symptoms include flattening of mood, anxiety, panic attacks, weeping, poor concentration and sleep disturbance. If this happens, it is vital that your partner's doctor or midwife is told right away. There are very real risks to mother and baby if this condition is ignored. Between three and ten per cent of mothers will need medical help for some degree of postnatal depression, and no-one is immune from it.

Bathing your baby

Soap a young baby on a towel on your lap before lowering her into the bath. Support her shoulders with one arm, holding her firmly around the top of her arm. Splash the water gently over her body with your other hand, and rinse off the soap. Wrap her straight in a warm towel on leaving the bath.

COPING WITH JEALOUSY

However much they may have been looking forward to the baby's arrival, many men begin to suffer pangs of jealousy when their child finally arrives home. The baby will inevitably take up an enormous proportion of the mother's time and attention. In addition, another human being is developing an intense physical relationship with their partner and many men find this genuinely troubling. Instead of being enthusiastic about the pleasure their partner gets from breastfeeding, they find feelings of jealousy creeping in. When bedtime also becomes too precious for sex – exhaustion and night feeds can certainly make this the case – then feelings of rejection are very understandable.

If you feel jealous, talk it over with your partner. The baby is helpless and needs her mother constantly – but this doesn't mean that you don't have needs too.

WHAT ABOUT SEX?

Almost every woman will feel somewhat bruised, sore and generally uncomfortable after childbirth. As in pregnancy, it is vital that you do not forget the importance of cuddling, holding and of romance. You are both going through all sorts of changes in your lives, and – however pleasurable parenthood might be – the stresses of these can affect your interest and ability in actual intercourse.

Once the soreness has gone, there is absolutely no reason why sexual relationships should not resume as soon as you both desire – there is no need to wait until your partner has had her six-week postnatal check-up. When you and your partner feel ready to consider actual intercourse, be particularly gentle and considerate. If you are in any way rough, it will inevitably hurt. Vaginal lubrication is always reduced for six to eight weeks after the birth, so additional lubrication such as KY Jelly can be very helpful. Most women have a decreased libido and need more time to become aroused in the first couple of months after childbirth. This could well be nature's way of preventing another pregnancy occurring too soon after a first pregnancy ends. Don't forget that your partner's breasts may be very tender if she is breastfeeding. And if intercourse hurts – stop!

A truly vicious circle may be set up if intercourse is painful. Soreness leads to anxiety, anxiety leads to a lessening of vaginal lubrication, and poor lubrication leads to soreness. So – take it gently, and take your time. If sexual discomfort, or poor libido, does persist, then your partner should certainly discuss this with her doctor. Sometimes very simple treatments can cure discomfort resulting from her episiotomy scar.

Remember that sleepless nights and hectically busy days with the baby can make your partner simply too tired for sex. Do be understanding if this is the case – things *will* improve. As in pregnancy, if you are kind and considerate, then your sexual relationship will have few problems.

NOW YOU'RE A FAMILY

Everything is different now that there are more than two of you. But don't forget that you and your partner should still be lovers and friends – not just mother and father to your children. Relationships suffer when all the attention and time goes into the children, and too little into the partner.

Make sure that you give time to your relationship. As soon as your partner feels confident to leave the baby with a sitter, take the opportunity to get out together for a few hours, whether it is for a meal, to the cinema, or just down to the pub. You both need space for yourselves as individuals, and for the continued development of your relationship. There is some evidence that men are better than women at giving themselves personal space and time. In that case, you owe it to your partner to ensure that she cares for herself as well as for your child. Every doctor is used to seeing mothers who are 'too busy looking after the family' to be ill, and who end up feeling shattered and exhausted. Don't let this happen to your partner.

There are many ways in which you can help to alleviate the baby's demands on your partner, and at the same time get to know your child intimately. The more you cuddle your baby, giver her a bath, change her nappy, and give her a bottle if she is bottle-fed, or if your partner expresses some milk, the more

Giving your baby a bottle *Bottle feeding your baby is a good opportunity to hold her close and cuddle her. To get her started on the bottle, touch her cheek with the teat, which triggers off the sucking reflex. Tilt the bottle slightly so that no air locks are created.*

A child's immunization timetable

Age	Immunization
From 2 months	Diphtheria Whooping cough Tetanus Polio
3 months	Diphtheria Whooping cough Tetanus Polio
4 months	Diphtheria Whooping cough Tetanus Polio
12-18 months	Measles Mumps Rubella (German measles)
About 5 years	Diphtheria (booster) Tetanus (booster) Polio (booster) Measles Mumps Rubella (if missed earlier)

practised and confident you will become and the closer the relationship with your child. Several aspects of practical fathering are illustrated on the pages of this chapter.

And many great days are ahead. The joys of Christmas and birthdays; the first words and the first faltering steps; that magical first trip to the seaside, and the intense anxiety of the first day at school. There will be pride in your child's achievements, and pleasure in the love that you give each other. It doesn't end on your child's wedding day either – or even on the day when you first discover that you are going to be a grandfather, and give your son a copy of a future edition of this book!

Fatherhood is as wonderful an experience as any human being can hope to undergo. So enjoy it – and good luck.

Registering the birth

It is the parents' responsibility to register a baby's birth within six weeks (three weeks in Scotland). To arrange this, go along to the local Registry Office, where the Registrar of Births, Marriages and Deaths will issue you with a birth certificate. Until you do this you will not be able to claim any benefits for the baby. As the child's father, and provided you are married to the mother, you can do this on your own. If you are not married to her, you will both need to attend together if you both wish to appear on the registration documents.

The Registrar will also give you a form with your baby's National Health Service number on it. Fill in the details and take it along to your G.P.'s surgery, to register her with the medical practice that you and your partner attend.

IMMUNIZATION

Most parents worry about immunization. They feel a great sense of responsibility for deciding which injections their baby should have, and then worry about whether they have made the right decision. It is therefore absolutely vital that you have all the information you possibly can when making your mind up. A leaflet will be available from your local clinic, and you and your partner should talk to your doctor or health visitor.

It is little wonder that parents get worried when they hear all the myths and stories – of brain damage, fits and so on – that circulate about immunization. Despite what you may hear, it is quite safe for children with eczema, or snuffly colds, to have all the injections. Indeed, it is almost always much safer to have your child immunized than to deprive her of the protection this brings. Diseases like whooping cough, diphtheria, tetanus and polio can kill or do permanent damage to your child's health. After all the trials and tribulations of pregnancy and childbirth, you owe it to your baby to give her the best protection.

The table opposite gives details of the various immunizations and the age at which your baby will be offered them. In some parts of the country the actual timing may be slightly different.

Useful addresses

When contacting these groups please do enclose a stamped addressed envelope. All of them can be extremely helpful and will offer valuable advice, but most are run by volunteers on limited funds.

Association for Improvements in the Maternity Services (AIMS)
40 King's Wood Avenue
London NW6 6LS
(081) 960 5585
Offers advice about rights, complaints procedures, and choices in antenatal and maternity care.

Child Poverty Action Group
4th Floor
1-5 Bath Street
London EC1V 9PY
(071) 253 3406
(2-4 pm, Mon-Thu)
Can offer advice about welfare and other benefits

Community Health Councils
See telephone directory for local addresses
Offer advice and help on any aspect of the National Health Service.

National Childbirth Trust
Alexander House
Oldham Terrace
Acton
London W3 6NH
(081) 992 8637
Runs antenatal classes giving advice on topics such as relaxation, massage and breathing techniques – amongst much else.

The Parent Network
44-46 Caversham Road
London NW5 2DS
(071) 485 8535
Aims to establish a national network of parent support groups.

CRY-SIS
BM Cry-sis
London WC1N 3XX
(071) 404 5011
A tremendous source of help for parents with a baby or child who cries excessively.

RELATE National Marriage Guidance
Herbert Gray College
Little Church Street
Rugby CV21 3AP
(0788) 73241

Confidential counselling service for people with relationship difficulties (see your telephone directory for local addresses)

Stillbirth and Neonatal Death Society (SANDS)
28 Portland Place
London W1N 4DE
(071) 436 5881
Self-explanatory, and a great support for bereaved parents.

Twins and Multiple Births Association
c/o Dr. Elizabeth Brian M.D.
at the Multiple Birth Foundation
The Queen Charlotte and
Chelsea Hospital
Goldhawk Road
London W6
(081) 748 4666
An extremely valuable group for any parents of twins, triplets or even more!

Index